SELECTED READINGS IN PHYSICS
General Editor: D. TER HAAR

MEN OF PHYSICS
LORD RAYLEIGH—
THE MAN AND HIS WORK

A

MEN OF PHYSICS

LORD RAYLEIGH
—THE MAN AND HIS WORK

BY

ROBERT BRUCE LINDSAY
Hazard Professor of Physics, Brown University

PERGAMON PRESS
Oxford · London · Edinburgh · New York
Toronto · Sydney · Paris · Braunschweig

1966

PERGAMON PRESS LTD.,
Headington Hill Hall, Oxford
4 & 5 Fitzroy Square, London W.1

PERGAMON PRESS (SCOTLAND) LTD.,
2 & 3 Teviot Place, Edinburgh 1

PERGAMON PRESS INC.,
Maxwell House, Fairview Park, Elmsford, New York 10523

PERGAMON OF CANADA LTD.,
207 Queen's Quay West, Toronto 1

PERGAMON PRESS (AUST.) PTY. LTD.,
19a Boundary Street, Rushcutters Bay, N.S.W. 2011, Australia

PERGAMON PRESS S.A.R.L.,
24 rue des Écoles, Paris 5e

VIEWEG & SOHN GMBH,
Burgplatz 1, Braunschweig

Library of Congress Catalog Card No. 79–94934

Printed in Great Britain by Page Bros. (Norwich) Ltd., Norwich

08 006820 0 (flexicover)
08 006821 9 (hard cover)

Contents

Preface

THE scientific career of John William Strutt, third Baron Rayleigh, spanned an unusually interesting period in the history of physical science. He was active during the last third of the nineteenth century and the first two decades of the twentieth. A man of vast erudition, broad interests and tremendous energy, he made important contributions to every field of physics known in his day. As a scientific statesman he labored mightily to improve the general public image of science.

The purpose of this book is to provide an appraisal of the significance of Rayleigh's scientific work together with extracts from his published papers. The task of selection has not been an easy one, since nothing he wrote was trivial. The effort here has been to concentrate on those achievements now known in all physics circles by his name. At the same time more attention has been paid to the basic physical content of the work than to the more severely mathematical papers.

The book is introduced with a brief biographical sketch, which necessarily leans heavily on *Life of John William Strutt, Third Baron Rayleigh* by his son, Robert John Strutt, Fourth Baron Rayleigh (second edition, edited by John N. Howard, University of Wisconsin Press, Madison, Wisconsin, 1968), to which the author's deep indebtedness is expressed. Part II is a critical evaluation of Rayleigh's scientific accomplishments. This is followed in Part III by extracts from twenty-three of Rayleigh's scientific papers, with brief editorial commentaries. These range in time from 1870 to 1919, the year of Rayleigh's death.

Grateful acknowledgement is made to Cambridge University Press and Dover Publications, Incorporated for permission to reprint selections and the bibliography from the collected "Scientific Papers" of Lord Rayleigh.

The author takes pleasure in acknowledging the kindness of the Honorable Charles Strutt, with whom he had interesting conversations about Lord Rayleigh (Mr. Strutt's Grandfather), and who showed him over the laboratory at Terling Place.

Providence, Rhode Island   R.B.L.

References to articles (e.g. Art. 47, etc.) in Part III refer to the numbered items of the bibliography.

PART I

Biographical Sketch of
John William Strutt, Third Baron Rayleigh
(1842-1919)

THE distinguished scientist who is the subject of this sketch occupies an unusual position in the history of British physics, if only because, while there are numerous examples of men raised to the peerage as a reward for outstanding scientific work, it is rare to find a peer by inheritance devoting himself to science. Lord Rayleigh was born John William Strutt, the eldest son of the second Baron Rayleigh of Terling Place, Witham, in the county of Essex. His immediate ancestors were country gentlefolk with little or no interest in scientific problems, though one of his grandmothers was descended from a brother of Robert Boyle. In his boyhood Rayleigh exhibited no unusual precocity but apparently displayed the average boy's interest in the world about him. His schooling was rather scattered, short stays at Eton and Harrow being terminated by ill health. He finally spent the four years preceding college at a small boarding school kept by a Rev. Mr. Warner in Highstead, Torquay, where he showed no interest in classics but began to develop decided competence in mathematics.

In 1861 at the age of nearly 20, young Rayleigh went up to Cambridge and entered Trinity College. Here he became a pupil of E. J. Routh, the famous "coach" in applied mathematics. It was under the guidance of Routh that he acquired the grasp of mathematics which stood him in such good stead in his later research. The system has often been criticized, but it ground the methods of advanced mathematical analysis essential for the physical scientist so thoroughly into the candidate that they became a natural part of his very being. It was not rigorous mathematics in the pure sense, but it was vigorous mathematics, which served to cultivate a keen appreciation of the particular method best suited for the solution of any particular problem. Rayleigh also stated in after life that he had profited greatly from the Cambridge lectures of Sir George G. Stokes, who though Lucasian Professor of Mathematics was greatly interested in experimental physics and performed many experimental demonstrations for his classes. In the Mathematical Tripos of 1865, Rayleigh came out as Senior Wrangler and also became first Smith's Prizeman. By this time he had clearly decided on a scientific career, though the propriety of this was considered by some members of his family rather doubtful in view of the social obligations inherent in his ultimate succession to his father's title and position. Rayleigh seems to have felt that such obligations should not be allowed to interfere with his scientific work. In 1866 he was elected Fellow of Trinity College, thus further emphasizing his scholarly leanings. Curiously enough he replaced the usual grand tour of the Continent with a trip to the United States, then in the throes of reconstruction after the Civil War.

In 1868, immediately after his return from America, Rayleigh purchased an outfit of experimental equipment. There was at that time no university physical laboratory, though certain professors possessed apparatus for their own experimental purposes and for demonstrations. Students received little or no direct encouragement to embark on experimental investigations for themselves. This may seem strange when one recalls that Cambridge had been for long the home of Newton. Moreover, long before Rayleigh's undergraduate days the immortal experiments of Young, Davy and Faraday, to mention only a few, had already shed undying lustre on British science. But this research had been carried on, by and large, outside the universities, which thus remained quite out of the current of real scientific progress in physics well past the first half of the nineteenth century. It was not until 1871 that Cambridge University established a professorship of experimental physics; in 1873 the Cavendish Laboratory was erected through the munificence of the Chancellor of the University, the eighth Duke of Devonshire. James Clerk Maxwell was elected the first

Cavendish professor and served from 1871 to his untimely death in 1879. For the first time practical instruction from a distinguished physicist was provided at Cambridge.

Since the following section of this book is devoted to a survey of the significance of Rayleigh's scientific work, there is no need to go into detail about it in this biographical sketch. It is sufficient to note that the young scientist's first serious research was experimental in character (on the galvanometer) and the results were presented in a paper at the Norwich meeting of the British Association for the Advancement of Science in 1868. This was the beginning of a lifetime of research, stimulated by his own curiosity but further by early careful reading of the current scientific literature, which provided many suggestions for independent investigation in the puzzles and questions left by previous researchers. Rayleigh's early experimental work was performed at the family estate at Terling with rather crudely improvised facilities. In those early days he was much encouraged by correspondence with Maxwell, who was always eager to help along a youthful colleague.

In 1871 Rayleigh married Evelyn Balfour, the sister of Arthur James Balfour, who was destined to achieve much celebrity as a scholar, philosopher and statesman. He had become acquainted with Balfour as a fellow student at Cambridge. Not long after his marriage a serious attack of rheumatic fever threatened for a time to cut short his career and left him much weakened in health. Somewhat surprisingly an excursion to Egypt was suggested as a recuperative measure, and a houseboat trip up the Nile was undertaken by the newly married couple late in 1872. Interestingly enough it was on this trip that Rayleigh's famous book *The Theory of Sound* had its genesis, the first part having thus been written without access to a large library. Shortly after the return to England in the spring of 1873, Strutt succeeded to the title and took up residence at Terling. It was then he introduced the laboratory where so much of his later experimental work was done. The installation was by no means an elaborate one, and visitors were inclined to wonder that such obviously important results could be obtained with what was considered even in his day to be rather crude equipment. But Rayleigh early manifested an economical turn of mind and took great pleasure in making inexpensively improvised apparatus yield precise results.

The premature death of Clerk Maxwell in 1879 left the Cavendish professorship vacant. Pressed by many scientific friends to stand for the post, Rayleigh finally consented, being partly influenced in his decision by the loss of income from his estate due to the agricultural depression of the late 1870s. It does not appear that he ever contemplated retaining the professorship for an indefinite period, and indeed he ultimately limited his tenure to five years. The pedagogical duties of the Cavendish professor were not onerous: he was required to be in residence for eighteen weeks during the academic year and to deliver at least forty lectures in the course of this period. Rayleigh, however, had no desire to interpret the job as a sinecure. He embarked vigorously on a program of developing elementary laboratory instruction in a really elaborate way. It is difficult to appreciate today what a task such a program involved some ninety years ago. Collegiate instruction in practical physics was almost a new thing, and there was little to go on save the teacher's imagination. Under Rayleigh's direction his demonstrators Glazebrook and Shaw, both of whom later became men of note, the former in applied physics and the latter in meteorology, developed laboratory courses for large classes in heat, electricity and magnetism, properties of matter, optics and acoustics. This was pioneer work of high order and had a beneficial influence on the teaching of physics throughout England and ultimately elsewhere.

The important scientific work carried out at Cambridge by Rayleigh and his collaborators on electrical standards will be reviewed in the next section of this book. At this point of the biographical sketch it will be of chief interest to note that the stay at Cambridge was a period of broadening professional and social relations, involving, for example, increasingly close acquaintance with fellow physicists like Sir William Thomson (later, and more familiarly known as, Lord Kelvin) and the American physicist and Johns Hopkins University professor, Henry A. Rowland. Through his relations by marriage Rayleigh was naturally brought into close contact with British politics and showed some, though scarcely any inordinate, interest in this primarily from the Conservative Party standpoint. He became, for example, a rather close friend of Lord Salisbury, several times Prime Minister.

During the Cambridge period Rayleigh greatly increased his interest in the affairs of the British Association and served as President of Section A (Mathematics and Physics) at the Southampton meeting in 1882. Before he vacated his professorship in 1884 he became even more closely involved, for he was asked to assume the presidency of the Association for the Montreal meeting in 1884, the first meeting held outside the United Kingdom. This meant a second trip to the North American continent, and Rayleigh took advantage of this to spend about two months touring both Canada and the United States. He was hospitably entertained by many American physical scientists, including Newcomb, Rowland, Trowbridge and Michelson.

Immediately after the return from the United States, Rayleigh resigned his professorship and went back to Terling, which remained his scientific headquarters for the rest of his life. In the meantime his financial position had improved, and he did not feel the need for the professional salary. Moreover, he must have felt that he could accomplish more as a lone scientific worker in home surroundings. It is true that there seems to have been a movement to get him to reconsider his resignation. It apparently will never be known how seriously he considered this.

Terling is close enough to London to permit frequent visits to the metropolis, so that Rayleigh could without too much inconvenience carry out official duties for governmental groups and professional societies to which he from time to time obligated himself and which ultimately became a significant part of his professional career. Though he clearly loved his laboratory, he was no recluse, and gave freely of his time and energy to endeavors for the advancement of science. Probably many contemporaries in the peerage as well as some tenants on his estate thought him rather queer for his preference for scientific activities, but Rayleigh went his own way with typical British imperturbability.

The life of a scientist working at his desk or in his laboratory has little of dramatic character to offer, at least to the man in the street. It is inevitable mankind in the large should find more emotional satisfaction in the contemplation of man's relations with his fellow creatures than in his association with the physical environment and his involvement with scientific ideas. For the most part, scientific investigations imply a train of reasoning unfamiliar and intricate to the general run of people. Occasionally, however, a scientific discovery will be made which involves a relatively simple and clear-cut situation, while at the same time it solves a puzzle originally as baffling as any detective story mystery. This was the case with the most dramatic popular episode in Rayleigh's career, namely the discovery of the rare gas argon in the atmosphere. The scientific details of the series of investigations involved in this will be found in the next section along with an account of some of the influences they had on Rayleigh's professional life, as well as speculations the discovery naturally arouses about the history of science.

In contemplating Rayleigh's career from the mid-1880s until his death in 1919 one cannot help marveling at the prodigious extent of his professional activity. He not only kept up a voluminous correspondence with active scientific colleagues like Lord Kelvin and Sir Arthur Schuster, but he continued to take a lively interest in society affairs. His interest in the British Association has already been mentioned. He had already served for eleven years (1885–96) as Secretary of the Royal Society of London in succession to Sir George Stokes. From 1905 to 1908 he was President of the Royal Society. In each case he took his duties very seriously. It was indeed during his term as secretary that he looked with care into the archives of the Society and made some discoveries of great historical interest. For example, he there discovered the celebrated paper by the Scottish amateur scientist J. J. Waterston on the kinetic theory of gases; this had been rejected by the Society for publication when it was presented in 1845 and had been lying hidden in the archives for over forty years. By exhuming it and calling attention to its significance, Rayleigh was able to do belated justice to a man who was really one of the founders of molecular physics.

Another activity in which Rayleigh took great satisfaction was his appointment in 1887 as Professor of Natural Philosophy at the Royal Institution of Great Britain on Albemarle Street in London. This institution, founded by the American Benjamin Thompson, Count Rumford, in 1800, for the purpose of encouraging popular interest in science and its useful applications, maintains laboratories for research in physics and chemistry as well as a lecture theater for the presentation of scientific results to lay audiences. It was here that Faraday made his epoch-making investigations in electromagnetism and electrochemistry. He also developed the art of popular science lecturing, with the famous Friday evening discourses and the equally famous series of Christmas lectures for children. The tradition thus established was very ably continued by John Tyndall, who, however, was forced to retire in the late eighties because of ill health. Rayleigh was invited to succeed him, and accepted the professional appointment with the understanding that he was not to be restricted in his experimental researches to the Institution's laboratories. He usually planned to work there during the London Easter season. During his tenure of the professorship from 1882 to 1905, Lord Rayleigh gave over 110 lectures in the afternoon series on a great variety of topics, usually popular presentations of the subjects in which he was or had been engaged in serious research. Sound, light and various aspects of electricity and magnetism formed the basis of most of the lectures, all of which were given extemporaneously with the help of brief notes and were illustrated by a wealth of experimental demonstrations. In addition he gave many evening lectures, which were also profusely illustrated. It is clear that Rayleigh took great interest in these lectures. His friend Sir Arthur Schuster says of him in this connection: "Though not by nature a ready speaker, his lectures were effective." Fortunately the essence of many of them has been preserved, included in his collected Scientific Papers. Probably the most famous of his evening discourses is the one on the discovery of argon.

In 1896 Lord Rayleigh was appointed Scientific Adviser to Trinity House, a very ancient organization dating back to the time of Henry VIII and having as its function the erection and maintenance of such coastal installations as lighthouses and buoys. For the next fifteen years he served faithfully in this capacity and made numerous inspection trips. Some of his later work in optics and acoustics was suggested by problems arising in connection with tests of lights and fog-signals. Rayleigh was always willing to give freely of his time and energy to deliberations of scientific committees of government and the various societies to which he belonged. For example, he was one of the leaders in the movement leading to the establishment of the National Physical Laboratory in Teddington (the British counterpart of the United States National Bureau of Standards), and presided over the Executive Committee of the Laboratory until shortly before his death. He also served as President of the Advisory Committee on Aeronautics from its inception in 1909 (at the instance of Prime Minister Asquith) until the time of his death. The activities of this committee were particularly important during the First World War (1914–18).

Other public services further reinforcing appreciation of Rayleigh's prodigious capacity for work include his Lord Lieutenancy of the County of Essex, involving responsibility for the selection of local magistrates, his chairmanship of the Explosives Committee of the War Office and his long tour of duty as Chief Gas Examiner for the London Gas Supply. At various times he served on the governing bodies of some half-dozen educational institutions, culminating in his appointment as Chancellor of Cambridge University in 1908, a post he held until his death.

In the midst of these multifarious activities and his never-ending scientific research, Rayleigh found time to arrange for the publication of his collected scientific papers and thus conferred a great boon on his successors in science as well as future historians of science. He personally supervised with meticulous care the publication of the first five volumes covering work done through

1910. The final volume, including the results of research done from 1911 to 1919, came out in 1920 under the editorship of his son. So valuable have these volumes proved for scholars and scientists that, the original editions having gone out of print, they were reprinted by Dover Publications (New York) in 1964, with the six volumes bound as three and with valuable notes and photographic illustrations under the editorship of John N. Howard of the United States Air Force Cambridge Research Laboratories of Bedford, Massachusetts. It is pertinent to recall in this connection that in 1963 the bulk of Rayleigh's experimental notebooks, calculations, rough notes and the original manuscripts of his published papers were acquired by the Laboratories and are now housed there as the Rayleigh Archives, together with photostats of his scientific correspondence. Copies of all this material have been placed in the library of the Imperial College of Science and Technology in the University of London and in the Niels Bohr Library of the History and Philosophy of Physics of the American Institute of Physics in New York. They are thus made adequately available for the use of scholars.

It might be thought that Rayleigh's many obligations would have kept him closely tied to home, with few opportunities for foreign travel. Such, however, was by no means entirely the case. In addition to his two visits to the United States and the Egyptian tour already mentioned, he and Lady Rayleigh toured India in 1897–8, partly in connection with a total eclipse of the sun visible there early in 1898. In 1908 the two visited South Africa and also made a trip up the East African coast. It must be confessed, though, that Rayleigh preferred life at Terling and in London to foreign travel. His tastes in recreation were simple, and he clearly never felt the need to develop any elaborate avocation separate from his scientific work; which he was fortunately able to keep up to the very end. He had a well-developed sense of humor and enjoyed witty stories. In fact he made a collection of these, which have been reprinted in the biography by his son.

Public recognition of his scientific attainments came to Lord Rayleigh in full measure. In 1904 he received the Nobel Prize in

Physics for his discovery of argon. He was one of the first recipients of the Order of Merit in 1902. Thirteen honorary degrees were conferred on him in addition to five other government awards. He was the recipient of awards by or honorary memberships in more than fifty learned societies.

As has already been pointed out, Rayleigh, unlike most scientists, had the good fortune to be able to continue his work until the very end of his life. He died at Terling on June 10, 1919, with three recently completed scientific papers still unpublished. Acoustical scientists will find interest in the fact that the very last of these was on acoustics. Rayleigh never got over his zest for problems in sound.

The opinion of his contemporaries and successors places Rayleigh in that great group of nineteenth-century physicists that have made British science famous all over the world; the group whose other members were Kelvin, Maxwell and Stokes. His position in the history of science is a great one. It is good to recall that he was above all a modest man, and it is impossible to treat as otherwise than sincere the remarks he made when he received the Order of Merit: "the only merit of which he personally was conscious was that of having pleased himself by his studies, and any results that may have been due to his researches were owing to the fact that it had been a pleasure to him to become a physicist."

PART II

Lord Rayleigh's Contributions to Science

Introduction

Lord Rayleigh was the last of the great polymaths of physical science. He outlived his closest rivals Helmholtz, Gibbs, Kelvin and Poincaré by a measurable span of years and remained professionally active to the very end of his life. His 445 published papers covered every field of physics known in his day with the possible exception of the atomic physics which began to flourish during the last two decades of his career. Rayleigh preferred to devote his attention to what is today referred to as "classical" physics, and in this broad area he never lacked interesting and worth-while problems.

Any estimate of Rayleigh's contributions to physics inevitably begins with a reference to his attitude toward research and the reasons for distributing his interest and effort as he did. His education at Cambridge was, of course, the classical variety common around the middle of the nineteenth century. The emphasis was on applied mathematics, more specifically mathematics applied to problems in the dynamics of particles and rigid bodies. Rayleigh's tutor was the well-known Edward Routh, and he got from this mentor a firm foundation in the effective use of mathematics. What physics there was in the instruction was largely confined to the contents of Newton's *Principia*. There was no laboratory work and the only university contact with experiments of any kind came through Stokes' lectures on light. Nevertheless young Strutt early showed great interest in experimentation, in the first instance through amateur photography. He would have liked to secure from Stokes hints as to interesting projects for research, but evidently received little encouragement. It seems that Rayleigh, like Maxwell, had to fall back on his own native, all-consuming curiosity about "the way things go" in laying out a program of scientific research.

Early Work

A glance at Rayleigh's first published papers indicates clearly that his earliest attempts at research were based on a careful study of what his reading of the scientific literature convinced him were important problems in physics. Thus he read Maxwell's great paper of 1865 on the dynamical theory of the electromagnetic field and was immediately stimulated to look for further analogies between electromagnetic and mechanical phenomena. This was the theme of his very first paper, "On Some Electromagnetic Phenomena considered in connexion with the Dynamical Theory", published in the *Philosophical Magazine* in 1869. At the same time he was reading widely in other fields, notably in the writings of Hermann von Helmholtz on sound. In 1860 Helmholz had studied the acoustic resonator now known everywhere by his name. Rayleigh felt he could improve the mathematical treatment considerably, and this formed the basis of his first excursion into acoustics. Interestingly enough he attacked the problem of the oscillations of the air in the mouth of the resonator from the standpoint of energy, thus following Maxwell in the latter's dynamical treatment of the electromagnetic field and employing a concept which was one of the great scientific constructs of the nineteenth century, but for which the terminology was only being settled at the time of Rayleigh's youth. In this study he also introduced the concept of the acoustic conductivity of an orifice, another illustration of the use of dynamical–electrical analogies. Rayleigh materially extended Helmholtz's results, including among other novelties a discussion of coupled resonators. This long paper, published in 1870 when Rayleigh was only 28 years of age, established his reputation as a scientist capable of handling a difficult physical problem in both its mathematical and experimental aspects.

Rayleigh returned frequently to acoustical problems during the seventies. His interest in the subject was further stimulated by his discovery around this time that there existed no up-to-date book on sound providing an adequate mathematical treatment of well-established experimental phenomena. There was indeed Helmholtz's famous treatise *Lehre von den Tonempfindungen* (1863), translated into English (1875) by A. J. Ellis under the title *Sensations of Tone*, but this specialized primarily in physiological and psychological acoustics and music. No one had taken the trouble to summarize in a single book the classical memoirs of Euler, Lagrange, D'Alembert, Bernoulli and the other theorists of the eighteenth century. To this task Rayleigh set himself. In the preliminary biographical sketch we have already described how he began his writing while he and his wife traveled in a houseboat on the Nile in 1872. About five years were devoted to the preparation of *The Theory of Sound*, one of the great classics of physical literature. The first volume, devoted primarily to the mechanics of vibrating media leading to the production of sound, appeared in 1877. This was followed in 1878 by a second volume treating of acoustic wave propagation. Rayleigh's continued interest in the subject during the next twenty years justified the preparation of an enlarged second edition, which appeared in 1892 and 1896. The popularity of the work and continued demand for it led to three subsequent reprintings (in 1926, 1929 and 1937 respectively). An American edition was brought out by Dover Publications, New York, in 1945, so that the classic work is still in print and serving the community of acoustical scientists. The significance of Rayleigh's work in acoustics for modern developments in the field is discussed at some length in the historical introduction to the Dover edition *Early Researches in Wave Phenomena*.

Wave phenomena of all kinds had a fascination for Rayleigh and this continued throughout his professional career. In addition to water waves, which fitted in appropriately with his interest in hydrodynamical problems in general, he found optics very much to his liking. In his many excursions into problems in light he[l] often found acoustical analogies fruitful; indeed, in reciproca fashion he made much use of optical analogies in his acoustical papers.

One of Rayleigh's earliest excursions into optics cleared up in decisive fashion a question which had long been obscure, namely the most appropriate explanation of the blue color of the sky. In a famous paper published in 1871 he derived the well-known law expressing the scattering of light by small particles as a function of the inverse fourth power of the wavelength of the incident light. This cleared up a puzzle which had received the attention, but more or less baffled the efforts, of a number of noted researchers, including Arago, Biot, Brewster, and Clausius. It was indeed the beautiful experimental researches of John Tyndall on the scattering of light by suspensions that probably served as the principal stimulus of Rayleigh's studies. In addition to the dependence of wavelength on scattering, Rayleigh was also able to predict theoretically the observed polarization of the scattered light. From the standpoint of the history of wave theory it is of interest to note that in his mathematical analysis Rayleigh employed the elastic solid theory of light rather than the electromagnetic theory, though he was of course familiar with Maxwell's prediction of the existence of electromagnetic waves moving in free space with the observed velocity of light. It is true that the theory of Maxwell was still in a highly speculative state and had not attracted much favorable attention; the experimental verification of Hertz was still to come. Though Rayleigh *was* definitely an innovator, he was a cautious one. He of course realized the fundamental difficulties inherent in the elastic solid theory, but he undoubtedly felt that this theory was adequate for the problem he was attacking. This was a shrewd and wholly justified estimate. This illuminates a trait that showed up early in this scientist's professional career and became more marked as he grew older: a kind of uncanny ability to feel how much could be got out of a given theory without indulging in too much elaborateness. In sheer imaginative power, Rayleigh did not reach the level of physicists like Einstein and Bohr, who were willing to launch forth on what many if not most contemporaries considered at first to be pure flights of fancy, and thus established brand new theories. Rayleigh was at his best at squeezing out of what was already available results which no one else thought could be attained.

Interest in Psychical Phenomena

In the early 1870s a good deal of interest developed in what is now called psychical phenomena. This interest was not confined to the naturally gullible and uneducated sections of the population. A number of scientists and scholars took it up, among them no less a reputable figure in science than William Crookes, who in the period 1870–3 devoted considerable attention to the phenomena produced in the presence of so-called "mediums". Though he abandoned his researches in this field after a few years it is believed he never in the future disavowed his conviction of the reality of some at least of the effects earlier observed. Crookes' reputation as a physical scientist was high and it is not surprising that his attitude encouraged others to look into these curious experiences in the attempt to provide a strictly scientific explanation. After Rayleigh inherited the title in 1873 and took up his residence with Lady Rayleigh at the family seat, Terling Place in Essex, he decided to try some psychical experiments for himself. This decision is evidence of his own well-developed curiosity as well as of his broadmindedness with respect to the kinds of human experience susceptible to scientific investigation. There is some reason to believe that if these early experiments had led to positive results, Rayleigh would have devoted a major share of his working time and effort to their further exploration, since he was of the opinion that if the results could be shown to be genuine their importance for human beings would justify the most thorough and careful study.

However, as Rayleigh revealed in his presidential address to the Society for Psychical Research in 1919 (the year of his death) and as has been amply verified by an examination of correspondence of an earlier date, he became disillusioned and unconvinced by such phenomena as he had witnessed in the 1870s. He therefore turned his attention exclusively to more conventional scientific research, even though throughout his life he appears to have kept an open mind about the need for more intensive exploration of these rather elusive phenomena.

Optical Instruments and the Laboratory at Terling

All through the 1870s Rayleigh's interest in optics was reflected in a series of researches in the construction and behavior of optical instruments. This work apparently originated around 1871 in his desire to fabricate cheap diffraction gratings by photographic means. His early experiments were not very successful, though he did succeed in copying original gratings by means of contact printing. This led him to the study of the resolving power of gratings, a subject not well understood in scientific circles at that time. In fact it seems clear that he himself was the first to publish in formal fashion a clear definition of resolving power and to carry out its evaluation for specific optical devices. Rayleigh was apparently the first to establish that the resolving power of a plane transparent grating is equal to the product of the order of the spectrum and the total number of lines in the grating. These studies culminated in a series of fundamental papers in the *Philosophical Magazine* in 1879 and 1880 on the optical properties of the spectroscope, an instrument then becoming of great importance in the study of the spectrum of the Sun as well as the spectra of chemical elements. In this connection it is also of interest to note that Rayleigh anticipated the French physicist Soret in the construction of the optical zone plate, with its interesting light-focusing properties, though he failed to publish this discovery for reasons which are not clear.

During the decade under discussion Rayleigh had installed a laboratory in his house at Terling and had developed what he considered to be a satisfactory work routine, dividing his time between experimental researches, in which he was assisted by a competent mechanician, and mathematical calculations in his study. He evidently preferred to have several projects in hand at once, turning from one to another as he felt inclined. It was rare for him to concentrate on one problem for long periods to the exclusion of all others. This method of working is reflected in the wide variety of problems treated in his published papers.

The Cambridge Period and Work on Electrical Standards

The Terling routine was interrupted in 1879 by two happenings: the first was the untimely death of James Clerk Maxwell, the first Cavendish Professor of Experimental Physics at Cambridge University, and the second was a severe agricultural depression in Britain, which materially reduced the income from Rayleigh's estate. When Sir William Thomson (later Lord Kelvin) refused to consider accepting appointment to the Cambridge vacancy, Rayleigh was the next obvious choice and was elected to the professorship in December 1879. Comment on his reorganization of undergraduate instruction in physics has already been made in the biographical sketch. Attention is concentrated here on the research program Rayleigh developed at Cambridge. He felt it appropriate to embark on a project suitable for group activity in order to interest advanced students. For this purpose he decided to redetermine the electrical standards, in particular the unit of resistance, the ohm, which had been originally standardized in 1863 by a committee of the British Association headed by Maxwell. The original equipment used in this determination was still available in Cambridge, and this fact may have helped to motivate the economy-minded Rayleigh. The apparatus used for the determination of the ohm was basically simple, viz. a circular coil of wire arranged to rotate uniformly about a vertical axis with a horizontal magnetic needle suspended at its center. Three precise measurements are essential to the evaluation, namely the diameter of the coil, the angular speed and the deflection of the magnetic needle. Since the ohm has the dimensions of velocity or distance divided by time, distance and time measurements are the ones fundamental in its determination. It soon developed in Rayleigh's laboratory that the old equipment was incompetent to provide the necessary precision. Hence new apparatus had to be built, and many fussy experimental difficulties had to be overcome. The work was not completed until near the end of 1881 and showed that the absolute ohm was 3 parts in 1000 less than the original B.A. unit. The detailed results were published in two lengthy memoirs in the *Proceedings of the Royal Society* for 1881 and the *Philosophical Transaction of the Royal Society* in 1882. Not entirely content with the standard B.A. method, Rayleigh turned to Lorenz's 1873 modification of the Faraday disc dynamo and carried out with this scheme in 1882 a long series of measurements in collaboration with his sister-in-law, Mrs. H. Sidgwick. The results were published in 1883 and agreed very well with those obtained by the original B.A. method. The determination of the ohm has stood up remarkably well in comparison with more recent measurements. Rayleigh's Cambridge involvement with electrical standards was concluded with a determination of the ampere by means of a current balance and silver voltameter, and the standardization of a Clark cell. This work undoubtedly served to influence Rayleigh favorably toward the establishment of a standards laboratory, which ultimately took the form of the National Physical Laboratory at Teddington.

Rayleigh did not allow his preoccupation with electrical standards at Cambridge to neglect other physical problems. Acoustics, hydrodynamics and the electromagnetic theory of light claimed a fair share of his attention. It was in this period that the Rayleigh disc for measuring the absolute intensity of sound was invented; it has remained a fundamental acoustical instrument ever since. He also initiated the study of acoustic streaming (direct current fluid motions in the neighborhood of an intense oscillating acoustic source) and thus began a development that is today proving of great importance in the biological application of sound waves. Other substantial research introduced the idea of surface waves on an elastic solid, since known as Rayleigh waves. A long memoir of 1881 laid the foundations for much future work on the scattering of electromagnetic radiation by particles. In this as in previous and subsequent research Rayleigh readily passed back and forth from optical to acoustical concepts, employing whatever analogies seemed to clarify his ideas and make his exposition of them more fruitful and forceful.

The relatively enormous number of papers (sixty in all) published during the Cambridge sojourn reflects a degree of activity scarcely equalled by any other eminent scientist working at that time. The record is all the more impressive in the light of the fact that nearly the whole of the final half year of his professorship was spent on a visit to Canada and the United States in connection with Rayleigh's presidency of the British Association at the Montreal meeting in the late summer of 1884.

Work at Terling in the Eighties.
Electromagnetic Theory, Black Body Radiation and
Intimations of Twentieth-century Physics

After the return to Terling early in 1885, the rest of Rayleigh's scientific career was largely spent in his laboratory and study there. The late eighties saw no real change in the well-established pattern of close attention to a wide variety of subjects of interest, both theoretical and experimental. Rayleigh was an avid reader of the physical literature of Western Europe and the United States, and much of his research had its origin in the questions and puzzles he encountered in his reading, sometimes of his own previous work. The opening paragraphs of many of his papers bear out this fact. In most cases he managed to shed new and useful light on the problems at issue and to suggest future lines of fruitful research. As an example from this period we may cite his 1887 paper on wave propagation through a medium endowed with a periodic structure, his interest in which he remarks was aroused by his earlier work on the colors of thin films. This was probably the first detailed investigation of what we now call wave filtration in iterated media, a field of great practical importance for the construction of both optical and acoustical filters. Rayleigh, indeed, did not use the word filtration; he preferred to describe his results in terms of selective reflection, but the filtration idea is implicit in his paper.

Rayleigh never lost his interest in electricity and magnetism and wrote a dozen papers in this general field during the period 1885–90, many of them devoted to magnetic properties of materials as well as self-induction. In acoustics this half decade saw substantial research into the production of sound by bells, to which Rayleigh himself attached considerable significance. However, the student of modern physics will undoubtedly show greater interest in the 1889 paper "On the Character of the Complete Radiation at a Given Temperature". This was Rayleigh's first excursion into the field of black body radiation, which in the hands of Planck was later to lead to the introduction of the quantum theory. Having had much to do earlier with finite wave trains and group velocity, he was impressed with the fact that to talk about the distribution of energy in the spectrum of black body radiation as a function of frequency implies, strictly speaking, saying something about what happens at a *single* frequency, which in turn demands an *infinite* wave train. He therefore attempted to consider that the black body radiation is to be represented as a random sequence of impulses of simple type. By this hypothesis he succeeded in obtaining the law by which H. F. Weber at that time was able to reproduce Langley's early experimental results, but the method was rather artificial and not too encouraging for further exploitation. As Rayleigh remarked many years later, after Planck had published his radiation formula: "the progress of knowledge with respect to the law of complete radiation is not favourable" to these earlier views of his. It is, of course, well known that in 1900 he derived by the use of the principle of equipartitions of energy applied to the expression for the number of discrete frequencies included in a given frequency interval in a closed space full of radiation in equilibrium, his celebrated inverse fourth power of wavelength law, since known as the Rayleigh–Jeans law. At that time he realized that this was a special case of the general Planck radiation law, valid for long wavelengths. Rayleigh was fully aware of the fundamental difficulties in the way of a classical explanation of the complete radiation law. Thus he had his own doubts about the general applicability of the principle of equipartition of energy. But at the same time he had no stomach for the quantum theory, and even though he did not attack it, felt it was foreign to his favorite way of thinking and should be left to younger men to exploit.

Rayleigh's interest in what in his day would be called "modern" physics was not confined to the black body radiation law. He early realized the significance of atomic theory in both chemistry and physics. This led him to attempt more precise measurements of the relative densities of the more prominent gases (hydrogen, oxygen and nitrogen) to try to obtain better values of relative atomic weights, which in terms of Prout's hypothesis should be in the form of ratios of small whole numbers. It was, of course, work of this sort, begun in 1887, that culminated in the discovery of argon as a constituent of the atmosphere. This research was a triumph of ingenuity in the choice and construction of equipment as well as patient perseverance in the face of puzzling difficulties. Rayleigh was always at his best when faced by a puzzle. When in 1892 in continuing his weighings of gases in the precision measurement of densities he found that the density of nitrogen prepared from ammonia was about one part in 200 less than the density of nitrogen obtained from air, this was a puzzle that appealed to him, and he did not let it go until he had cleared it up.

The Discovery of Argon

The discovery of argon is admitted by all to have been the most dramatic episode in Rayleigh's scientific career. It involved a difficult and time-consuming investigation, demanding infinite patience in order to secure the necessary precision with equipment which today would be considered totally inadequate for the purpose in hand. And in the course of the investigation Rayleigh was made rather unhappy by the fact that another investigator, the chemist Sir William Ramsay, decided to pursue his own

B

independent study of the density anomaly which Rayleigh had turned up and which he had freely published in the literature. This raises an interesting question in the history of science. Should Rayleigh have refrained from *any* publication of his early density results until he himself had worked out the probable consequences? If he had done this, the whole credit for the resulting discovery would have been his alone, unless by sheer accident someone else had happened simultaneously to hit on the same anomaly and had decided to investigate it further. As a matter of historical fact, someone else *had* come very close to the discovery of argon a hundred years before. This was Henry Cavendish, who in 1795 had oxidized the nitrogen in the air by sparking the air enclosed in a vessel as far as he could; he always in his experiments found a very small amount of gas left over which could not be oxidized. Hence he must have realized that there is a constituent of the atmosphere which is different from oxygen, nitrogen and carbon dioxide. But Cavendish never checked his results to make sure of their validity. Moreover, he was forced to use relatively poor electrical equipment (an early static machine). There is no indication that he felt seriously inclined to follow up his results; he probably considered that the residual gas was too scanty in quantity to be of much significance.

However, it was a reading of Cavendish's 1795 paper (probably suggested by Sir James Dewar, though it is difficult to establish this with complete assurance) that apparently gave Rayleigh the clue to the step which ultimately made him sure he had discovered a new constituent of the atmosphere. But while Rayleigh was using Cavendish's physical method of sparking air with oxygen to get rid of the nitrogen and thus ultimately isolate the residual constituent, Ramsay had begun to use chemical means to achieve the same end; he employed the reaction between nitrogen and magnesium. In this way he succeeded in isolating the unknown gas faster than Rayleigh did, though not, so far as is known, before Rayleigh. The relation between the work of the two investigators, performed in different places by different methods but at approximately the same time, naturally gave rise to much speculation and discussion with resulting embarrassment to both men. So far as can be ascertained from the recollections of those close to the two scientists involved, Rayleigh felt that he had not been asked by Ramsay whether he, Rayleigh, objected to Ramsay's carrying out of an independent investigation of the problem after he had learned through the periodical literature what Rayleigh was doing. Hence Rayleigh took the stand that he had *not* given permission since no permission had been asked. However, in spite of this, his public position seems to have been that Ramsay had a perfect right to pursue his investigations independently. On the other side, there seems to exist the general impression that Ramsay felt he had in effect asked permission to proceed, and that such permission had been granted. Standard scientific etiquette would suggest that as soon as a scientist has revealed in the open literature what he is doing and has even, as was true in Rayleigh's case, publicly asked scientific colleagues for suggestions with respect to the puzzle facing him, it is perfectly proper for anyone else who finds the problem interesting to take it up for himself; he is under no obligation to notify anyone of what he is about until he is ready to publish definitive results. Of course, he may well find it to his advantage to report progress and tentative results at scientific meetings and the like in order to avoid the possibility of the unnecessary expenditure of time and money, but the choice should be free. It is probable that Rayleigh shared this view, as his whole career seems to indicate that he was more interested in the scientific results for themselves than in the fame they might bring to him, though he was apparently human enough not to be averse to the recognition by his scientific colleagues of the work he had done.

In any case, it is a fact that Ramsay kept Rayleigh minutely informed of the progress of his investigations and the relations between the two men remained cordial. The results were announced in a joint publication in 1894; it was clear to all that there was enough honor to go around! It is perhaps sufficient to recall that ten years after the publication Rayleigh received the Nobel Prize in Physics, largely on the basis of his discovery of the hitherto unknown constituent of the atmosphere, while at the same time Ramsay received the Nobel Prize in Chemistry, partly for his share in the discovery of argon, but also for his elaborate further work on the other rare gases of the atmosphere and notably the terrestrial existence of helium. Rayleigh did not choose to follow up this line to any serious extent; he did not esteem his competence as a chemist very highly. Moreover, it is clear he had found the whole course of the argon research a very fatiguing business and was doubtless glad of the chance to return to the less physically demanding routine of experimental and theoretical work which formed the basis of his scientific life at Terling.

There is another aspect of the discovery of argon which warrants attention: this is the scepticism with which the discovery was received, not only by the educated lay public as represented by the London *Times*, but also by many well-known chemists and physicists. The chemists in general were the ones who expressed the greatest doubts about the validity of the claim made by Rayleigh and Ramsay. This was probably to be expected, since it seemed somehow incredible to many that all the previous work on the nature of the atmosphere from the time of Cavendish, a full century earlier, could have completely missed such a vital point. To some critics it seemed reasonable to suppose that the gas which was claimed to be a hitherto undetected constituent of the atmosphere was actually the result of some previously unobserved chemical reaction—a new chemical compound in short. The reluctance of the new gas to combine with any known elements served to silence most of the critics, though the objections continued to persist for some little time. The name argon was given to the new gas in token of its chemical inertness. Many attempts were made to get the new gas to combine chemically with other substances, but without success, as detailed in the joint paper which Rayleigh and Ramsay contributed to the *Philosophical Transactions of the Royal Society* in 1895. At the very end of the paper the suggestion was made that fluorine be tried, though neither author felt inclined to carry this out. It was not until 1961 that argon hexafluoride was actually made.

Further Work in Light and Sound

During the three years in which Rayleigh pursued his investigations leading to the discovery of argon, he still found time to contribute to the scientific literature some twelve papers dealing with other problems. Most of these concerned the interference and scattering of light, though two related to the behavior of the telephone, then attracting much attention particularly from the standpoint of its sensitivity. Rayleigh tried to construct a theory of the telephone, though he confessed that there were too many uncertain factors to make it really satisfactory. An important acoustical by-product, however, was an attempt to estimate experimentally the minimum audible intensity of sound in the open air. Using a tuning-fork as a source and assuming spherical waves, Rayleigh found a figure of about 10^{-13} watt/cm^2. When it is considered that he was the only observer and that he was about 50 years old at the time, this cannot be considered such a bad result compared with the presently accepted average of 10^{-16} watt/cm^2. At any rate, Rayleigh's realization of the importance of this figure is another indication of his foresight with respect to the future of physics.

Another example of Rayleigh's uncanny ability to forecast future developments in physics is found in his 1899 paper "On the Cooling of Air by Radiation and Conduction, and on the Propagation of Sound". Here he examined certain American measurements of sound attenuation in air indicating the existence of much greater absorption than could be explained by the usual classical theory of sound absorption due to viscosity and heat conduction. Rayleigh suggested that the anomaly might ultimately find its explanation in a molecular theory of sound absorption in which the mechanism is relaxation between translational and internal (vibrational and rotational) energy states of the molecules of the absorbing gas. This suggestion was taken up by J. H. Jeans in his *Dynamical Theory of Gases* (1904), but was not exploited in detail until the researches of Einstein, Rice, Herzfeld and Kneser in the twenties and thirties of the twentieth century. Study of such relaxation mechanisms has now become a standard technique not only in the understanding of acoustic attenuation in fluids and solids, but also in the use of sound attenuation measurements for the exploration of molecular structure and interaction.

Rayleigh's interest in electrical problems during the late 1890s led him among other things to lay the foundation for wave guide analysis, which turned out to be so fundamental for the future of microwave transmission. In all this work he continually stressed the analogies between acoustic and electric radiation. Of similar significance was his pioneer work on the reflection of radiation from rough or corrugated surfaces. This has proved of great value to workers in underwater sound.

Rayleigh and Modern Physics

In any critique of Rayleigh's scientific work, one is inevitably faced with the problem of his relation to modern physics as represented by the invention and development of relativity and quantum theory. We have already touched on this briefly in connection with the general black body radiation law. Rayleigh realized keenly the difficulties in the way of a classical attack on this problem, but he felt himself unable to accept what he considered to be highly speculative hypotheses like that of Planck, having no root in classical physics. He evidently preferred to hope that explanations of new and somewhat bizarre experience might still be found along classical lines if only one were patient and clever enough. This feeling seems to provide the key to Rayleigh's attitude toward twentieth-century physics. It was not that he lacked interest in the more novel approaches: he examined them all carefully, for his reading was wide; but never became happy with them. A more detailed examination of his research in the period from 1890 to the time of his death will justify this appraisal.

Let us look first at regularities in optical series spectra. The obvious classical attack on this problem was through the natural frequencies of vibrations of mechanical or electrical systems of many degrees of freedom. This was a field in which Rayleigh excelled. In a paper entitled "On the Propagation of Waves along Connected Systems of Similar Bodies" published in the *Philosophical Magazine* in 1897, he examined among other cases a system of connected rotating magnets, proposed by Fitzgerald as a possible source of radiation. The analysis leads to a formula for the natural frequencies which with the use of a suitable and plausible approximation can be made to agree with the Balmer formula for the frequencies of the lines in the hydrogen spectrum. This might have seemed encouraging, but, as Rayleigh himself remarks, such efforts at explanation of spectral series cannot carry much conviction, since in practically all cases involving classical vibrating systems the frequencies come out as the square roots of expressions involving integers, whereas spectral frequencies are exactly expressible without the use of square roots, as is abundantly clear in the case of the Balmer and similar series. Fitzgerald's example was an odd and rather artificial one with the integral frequencies expressed in terms of a transcendental function, so that the fit with observed spectral frequencies could be only approximate at best. This observation of Rayleigh, simple though it was and possibly made with a feeling of mild frustration, may well have had considerable influence in discouraging further research along the line of classical vibration analogies as a possible explanation for series spectra. On the other hand, though Rayleigh read Bohr's fundamental papers on the quantum theory of atomic structure with great interest, it is clear that he felt unable to go along with Bohr's rather radical type of physical theorizing. As he is said to have remarked of this: "It does not suit me."

It is important to recall at this point that Rayleigh did not dismiss entirely the subject of spectra from his consideration with the completion of the work just reviewed. He actually returned to the problem in 1906 in an interesting paper "On Electrical Vibrations and the Constitution of the Atom." Here he investigated the atom model of Sir J. J. Thomson from the standpoint of both stability and the emission of radiation. He ran once more into the same difficulty with respect to the emitted frequencies (the "square root" problem) which he had stressed in his earlier article already mentioned. The later paper has particular interest because of the reference to atomic models in which electrons move in orbits. Rayleigh saw no likelihood that spectral regularities could be accounted for through ordinary electromagnetic radiation from such electron motions. The final sentence in this article is significant enough in the light of later developments to warrant quoting: "The frequencies observed in the spectrum may not be frequencies of disturbance or of oscillations in the ordinary sense at all, but rather form an essential part of the original constitution of the atom as determined by conditions of stability." One is led to wonder whether Niels Bohr ever read this paper!

It is an interesting fact that even though Rayleigh refused to participate directly in the theoretical developments that led to modern quantum mechanics, some of his work created with quite different ideas in mind has proved of great value in this theory. An example is the so-called adiabatic principle, made much of by Ehrenfest and applied by Bohr and others to the perturbation of atomic systems by external influences like magnetic and electric fields. In this connection the interested reader is advised to read Rayleigh's paper "On the Pressure of Vibrations" in the *Philosophical Magazine* (1902), in which in examining radiation pressure he effectively establishes the adiabatic invariant in the case of the slow shortening of the string of a vibrating simple pendulum. It is true that he does not stress the invariance aspect, but it is clearly implicit in this and other illustrations. It may be recalled that the case of the pendulum provides the standard method of introducing the concept of adiabatic invariance in texts on atomic theory.

Another illustration of the modern utility of Rayleigh's researches is the so-called Rayleigh–Ritz method for the approximate evaluation of the normal modes of a complicated vibrating system. Rayleigh anticipated Ritz, who developed the method in greater detail. This is a standard method for the calculation of the eigenvalues of quantum mechanical Schrödinger equations.

Rayleigh and Relativity

Somewhat greater interest probably inheres in Rayleigh's concern over the physical problems that ultimately led to the establishment of the theory of relativity. In 1887, in preparation for his article "Wave Theory" for the *Encyclopædia Britannica*, he wrote a section on astronomical aberration. This indeed was not finally included in the encyclopedia article but was published separately in *Nature* in 1892. In this paper Rayleigh took up in detail the bearing of astronomical aberration on the theory of a luminiferous ether, concluding that the observational evidence indicated the validity of Fresnel's hypothesis of a stationary ether. Rayleigh did call attention to Michelson's attempt (1881) to test Maxwell's suggestion that the time for light to travel a given distance would vary depending on the direction of the light beam. Though Michelson considered that his first experiment (made with his famous interferometer) showed that the presumed dependence does not actually exist, in contradiction to Fresnel's hypothesis, Rayleigh in his paper expressed the feeling that Michelson's work was too fraught with difficulties to make his conclusion convincing. However, in the meantime Michelson had repeated the experiment (this time with Morley) in 1887 and the two collaborators concluded that the new results also contradicted the hypothesis of a stationary ether. This work unfortunately appeared too late for Rayleigh to incorporate it in his article on aberration, and when he finally published the paper in 1892 he failed to make a specific reference to the 1887 Michelson–Morley experiment. He merely warned the reader that Michelson's work would have to be considered in any final assessment of the situation. It seems clear from Rayleigh's correspondence with Michelson, Lorentz, Lodge and others in the early 1890s that he still felt doubtful about the cogency of the results of the Michelson–Morley experiment; at any rate he evidently hoped there would emerge some way of interpreting it which would not contradict the hypothesis of a stationary ether. He realized the very great importance of the whole problem and was puzzled and disturbed by obvious inconsistencies; his loyalty to the classical wave theory of light made him hesitate to give up the latter without more definite experimental evidence.

Rayleigh's continued concern with the ether problem is evidenced by his attempt in 1902 to detect possible double refraction in a material medium due to its motion through a presumptive stationary ether. He studied both liquids and solids in this connection and came to the conclusion that no such double refraction is observable. This experiment, along with that of Michelson and Morley and others about this period, provided further background for the introduction of the theory of special relativity by Lorentz, Poincaré and Einstein. Rayleigh produced no further papers in this subject. There is evidence that he read the writings of the relativists with interest, but he did not feel he had anything to contribute to the theory as such. Once again his conservative tendency asserted itself.

The Later Years

An unusual characteristic of Rayleigh's scientific career was that he showed no slackening of his research activity after he reached the age of 60, when the majority of scientists feel that their work is done. Actually, 164 papers were published between 1903 and 1919, the year of his death. Though many of these were obvious extensions of early work, many were definitely significant and some have proved to be fundamental. There was scarcely a field in which Rayleigh had been interested as a young man to which he did not return in his later years. The two fields in which he retained primary interest were, of course, acoustics and optics: in these he brought out some ninety papers in the last sixteen years of his life. Some of these deserve comment.

In acoustics we may call attention to the long 1910 paper on "Aerial Plane Waves of Finite Amplitude", which is not only a remarkably comprehensive review of the whole subject (including material treated briefly earlier in the *Theory of Sound*), but includes the result of pioneer research on the formation and behavior of shock waves, going well beyond the earlier investigations of

Rankine and Hugoniot by considering the effect of viscosity and heat conduction on waves of discontinuity. To be sure, in this paper Rayleigh does not use the word "shock" wave, but this is what he is really talking about.

A similar piece of pioneer research was involved in Rayleigh's return in 1907 to his concern of some thirty years earlier for the perception by human beings of sound direction. He soon convinced himself that the binaural effect cannot be accounted for at all frequencies on the basis of difference in intensity at the two ears, but that phase differences also enter vitally into the phenomenon, particularly at low frequencies. This set the stage for an impressive development in physiological and psychological acoustics, which, however, did not get underway for another decade or more. Here again we glimpse in Rayleigh an uncanny ability to derive effective results from a judicious combination of theory and experiment, the latter always seemingly simple in design and construction but never failing to get at the heart of the matter.

Rayleigh's interest in the diffraction and scattering of sound is further reflected in his return in 1904 to a consideration of the problem of the acoustic shadow of a rigid sphere, extending materially his earlier work on this subject in *The Theory of Sound*. In this work he calculated the scattering for the rather difficult case in which the wavelength is of the same order of magnitude as the radius of the sphere. Another important paper of the later years was the 1912 article "On the Propagation of Waves through a Stratified Medium with special reference to the Question of Reflection". Here Rayleigh considered again what we now refer to as sound filtration, a very important problem in modern acoustics, though he failed to use this terminology. As was customary in his writings he calls attention to the basic analogy between acoustical and optical propagation. This analogy is further emphasized in the papers discussing wave diffraction by the passage of radiation through narrow slits in an otherwise opaque screen.

Wave scattering in general always had a fascination for

Rayleigh. His very early paper on the blue color of the sky is a good example. He returned to this problem in great detail in his 1899 paper "On the Transmission of Light through an Atmosphere containing Small Particles in Suspension and on the Origin of the Blue of the Sky". This was a somewhat delayed response to a query by Maxwell back in the 1870s whether the explanation of the color of the sky demands scattering by macroscopic particles in suspension in the atmosphere or whether scattering by the very molecules of the gases of the atmosphere will not answer equally well. Rayleigh's analysis showed that the latter assumption is indeed a plausible one, though scattering by the molecules alone will provide a somewhat darker blue sky than actually observed. Hence some macroscopic suspensions are probably also involved.

A good illustration of Rayleigh's helpfulness in shedding useful light on a puzzling problem is provided by his 1905 article "The Origin of the Prismatic Colours". He starts with the well-known question about which there had been considerable controversy: when so-called white light is dispersed by a prism or grating, are the colors which are then observed already existent in the incident light, or are they really made by the passage through the instrument? Rayleigh realized that the question had actually been rather decisively answered by Schuster and Ames, but he still found some interesting points outstanding and proceeded to study in detail the resolution of a wave pulse into its Fourier components, a procedure of great value in subsequent electronic research.

Rayleigh's profound insight into radiation scattering is shown nowhere more effectively than in his fundamental paper of 1907: "On the Dynamical Theory of Gratings." Here the problem is treated from the standpoint of reflection from a corrugated surface, somewhat along the lines of his earlier acoustical investigations. This enabled him to solve the limiting case in which the grating space is less than the wavelength of light, for which the ordinary optical theory of Fresnel with its emphasis solely on the interference of diffracted light yields nothing but effectively specular reflection. By setting up the boundary conditions for the incidence of a plane wave on a periodic corrugated surface Rayleigh was able to obtain the scattered wave for any period of the surface. Thus he combines in one package, so to speak, the solution of the complete plane grating problem in optics and the transmission of underwater sound as affected by an idealized rough sea surface.

General Comments. Rayleigh's Style

This review of Rayleigh's scientific work would be incomplete without some reference to the style of his published articles. He wrote with easy grace and with a relaxed and almost conversational style. It was his habit to introduce each article with prefatory remarks indicating why he was engaged in the research whose results he was presenting. These introductions are very helpful in providing a background for an appreciation of his thinking; much of the history of the physics of Rayleigh's time is implied in them. They are worth reading even by those who are in no position to follow the scientific details of the body of the articles, which as a rule assume considerable acquaintance with theoretical physics on the part of the reader. Having said this, we must admit that Rayleigh rarely provided adequate summaries of his results at the ends of articles. This is unfortunate as it detracts for the general scientific reader from a just understanding of Rayleigh's accomplishments. We ought to mention the summaries of his Royal Institution Lectures which are included in his collected papers. These are extremely well written, and might well be collated and published in a separate volume.

Bibliography of the Writings of Lord Rayleigh

THIS is the complete chronological bibliography of the writings as prepared by Rayleigh for the collected edition of his scientific papers. It also includes his treatise *The Theory of Sound*. At the left of each item is the number of the corresponding article in Rayleigh's *Scientific Papers* (six volumes bound as three, New York, Dover Publications, Inc., 1964).

An asterisk precedes the title of each paper reproduced in whole or part in the present volume.

1. On some Electromagnetic Phenomena considered in connexion with the Dynamical Theory
   [*Phil. Mag.* xxxviii, pp. 1–15, 1869.]

2. On an Electromagnetic Experiment
   [*Phil. Mag.* xxxix, pp. 428–435, 1870.]

3. On the values of the Integral $\int_0^1 Q_n Q_n' d\mu$, Q_n, Q_n' being Laplace's Coefficients of the orders n, n', with an application to the Theory of Radiation
   [*Phil. Trans.* clx, pp. 579–590; read June 1870.]

4. Remarks on a paper by Dr Sondhauss
   Postscript
   [*Phil. Mag.* xl, pp. 211–217, 1870.]

*5. On the Theory of Resonance
   Introduction

   Part I
   Several Openings
   Double Resonance
   Open Organ-pipes
   Long Tube in connexion with a Reservoir
   Lateral Openings

   Part II
   Long Tubes
   Simple Apertures
   Cylindrical Necks
   Potential on itself of a uniform Circular Disk
   Nearly Cylindrical Tubes of Revolution
   Upper Limit
   Application to straight Tube of Revolution whose ends lie on two infinite Planes

Tubes nearly Straight and Cylindrical but not necessarily of Revolution
Tubes not nearly Straight

Part III
Experimental
[*Phil. Trans.* CLXI, pp.77–118; read Nov. 1870.]

6. Note on the explanation of Coronas, as given in Verdet's *Leçons d'Optique Physique*, and other works
[*London Math. Soc. Proc.* III, pp. 267–269, 1871.]

7. Some Experiments on Colour
Yellow
[*Nature*, III, pp. 234–237, 264, 265, 1871.]

*8. On the Light from the Sky, its Polarization and Colour
Appendix
[*Phil. Mag.* XLI, pp. 107–120, 274–279, 1871.]

9. On the Scattering of Light by small Particles
[*Phil. Mag.* XLI, pp. 447–454, 1871.]

10. On Double Refraction
[*Phil. Mag.* XLI, pp. 519–528, 1871.]

11. On the Reflection of Light from Transparent Matter
[*Phil. Mag.* XLII, pp. 81–97, 1871.]

12. On a Correction sometimes required in Curves professing to represent the connexion between two Physical Magnitudes.
[*Phil. Mag.* XLII, pp. 441–444, 1871.]

13. On the Vibrations of a Gas contained within a Rigid Spherical Envelope.
[*London Math. Soc. Proc.* IV, pp. 93–103, 1872.]

14. Investigation of the Disturbance produced by a Spherical Obstacle on the Waves of Sound
[*London Math. Soc. Proc.* IV, pp. 253–283, 1872.]

15. Notes on Bessel's Functions
[*Phil. Mag.* XLIV, pp. 328–344, 1872.]

16. On the Reflection and Refraction of Light by Intensely Opaque Matter
[*Phil. Mag.* XLIII, pp. 321–338, 1872.]

17. Preliminary note on the Reproduction of Diffraction-Gratings by means of Photography
[*Proc. Roy. Soc.* XX, pp. 414–417, 1872.]

18. On the Application of Photography to copy Diffraction-Gratings
[*Brit. Assoc. Report*, 1872, p. 39.]

19. On the Diffraction of Object-Glasses
[*Astron. Soc. Month. Not.* XXXIII, pp. 59–63, 1872.]

20. An Experiment to illustrate the Induction on ʰself of an Electric Current
     [*Nature*, VI, p. 64, 1872.]

21. Some General Theorems relating to Vibrations

     Section I
     The natural periods of a conservative system, vibrating freely about a configuration of stable equilibrium, fulfil the stationary condition

     Section II
     The Dissipation Function

     Section III
     [*London Math. Soc. Proc.* IV, pp. 357–368, 1873.]

22. On the Nodal Lines of a Square Plate
     [*Phil. Mag.* XLVI, pp. 166–171, 246, 247, 1873.]

23. Note on a Natural Limit to the Sharpness of Spectral Lines
     [*Nature*, VIII, pp. 474, 475, 1873.]

24. On the Vibrations of Approximately Simple Systems
     [*Phil. Mag.* XLVI, pp. 357–361, 1873; XLVIII, pp. 258–262, 1874.]

25. On the Fundamental Modes of a Vibrating System
     [*Phil. Mag.* XLVI, pp. 434–439, 1873.]

26. Vibrations of Membranes
     [*London Math. Soc. Proc.* V, pp. 9, 10, 1873.]

27. Harmonic Echoes
     [*Nature*, VIII, pp. 319, 320, 1873.]

28. Note on the Numerical Calculation of the Roots of Fluctuating Functions
     [*London Math. Soc. Proc.* V, pp. 119–124, 1874.]

29. A History of the Mathematical Theories of Attraction and the Figure of the Earth from the time of Newton to that of Laplace. By I. Todhunter, M.A., F.R.S. Two Volumes. (London, Macmillan & Co., 1873.)
     [*The Academy*, V, pp. 176, 177, 1874.]

*30. On the Manufacture and Theory of Diffraction-Gratings
     [*Phil. Mag.* XLVII, pp. 81–93, 193–205, 1874.]

31. Insects and the Colours of Flowers
     [*Nature*, XI, p. 6, 1874.]

32. A Statical Theorem
     [*Phil. Mag.* XLVIII, pp. 452–456, 1874; XLIX, pp. 183–185, 1875.]

33. Mr Hamilton's String Organ
     [*Nature*, XI, pp. 308, 309, 1875.]

34. General Theorems relating to Equilibrium and Initial and Steady Motions
[*Phil. Mag.* XLIX, pp. 218–224, 1875.]

35. On the Dissipation of Energy
[*Proc. Roy. Inst.* VII, pp. 386–389, 1875; *Nature*, XI, pp. 454, 455, 1875.]

36. On the Work that may be gained during the Mixing of Gases
[*Phil. Mag.* XLIX, pp. 311–319, 1875.]

37. Vibrations of a Liquid in a Cylindrical Vessel
[*Nature*, XII, p. 251, 1875.]

38. On Waves
The Solitary Wave
Periodic Waves in Deep Water
Oscillations in Cylindrical Vessels
[*Phil. Mag.* I, pp. 257–279, 1876.]

39. On the Approximate Solution of Certain Problems relating to the Potential
[*London Math. Soc. Proc.* VII, pp. 70–75, 1876.]

*40. Our Perception of the Direction of a Source of Sound
[*Nature*, XIV, pp. 32, 33, 1876.]

41. Questions from Mathematical Tripos Examination for 1876
January 6.   9 –12
January 6. $1\frac{1}{2}$– 4
January 17.   9 –12
January 19. $1\frac{1}{2}$– 4
January 20. $1\frac{1}{2}$– 4
January 21.   9 –12
January 21. $1\frac{1}{2}$– 4
[*Cambridge University Calendar*, 1876.]

42 .On the Resistance of Fluids
[*Phil. Mag.* II, pp. 430–441, 1876.]

43. Notes on Hydrodynamics
The Contracted Vein
Meeting Streams
[*Phil. Mag.* II, pp. 441–447, 1876.]

*44. On the Application of the Principle of Reciprocity to Acoustics
[*Proc. Roy. Soc.* XXV, pp. 118–122, 1876.]

45. On a Permanent Deflection of the Galvanometer-Needle under the influence of a rapid series of equal and opposite Induced Currents
[*Phil. Mag.* III, pp. 43–46, 1877.]

The Theory of Sound
[Two volumes, London, Macmillan & Company, 1877, 1878. Second revised and enlarged edition, 1892 and 1896. Reprinted 1926, 1929, and 1937. First American edition, two volumes bound as one, New York, Dover Publications, Inc., 1945.]

Points of Silence near a Wall from which a Pure Tone is reflected
Sensitive Flames
Aerial Vibrations of very Low Pitch maintained by Flames
Rijke's Notes on a large scale
Mutual Influence of Organ-Pipes nearly in Unison
Kettledrums
The Æolian Harp
[*Phil. Mag.* vii, pp. 149–162, 1879.]

62. Investigations in Optics, with special reference to the Spectroscope
§ 1. Resolving, or Separating, Power of Optical Instruments
§ 2. Rectangular Sections
§ 3. Optical Power of Spectroscopes
§ 4. Influence of Aberration
§ 5. On the Accuracy required in Optical Surfaces
§ 6. The Aberration of Oblique Pencils
§ 7. Aberration of Lenses and Prisms
§ 8. The Design of Spectroscopes
[*Phil. Mag.* viii, pp. 261–274, 403–411, 477–486, 1879; ix, pp. 40–55, 1880.]

63. On Reflection of Vibrations at the Confines of two Media between which the Transition is Gradual
[*London Math. Soc. Proc.* xi, pp. 51–56, 1880.]

64. On the Minimum Aberration of a Single Lens for Parallel Rays
[*Cambridge Phil. Soc. Proc.* iii, pp. 373–375, 1880.]

65. Acoustical Observations. III
Intermittent Sounds
A New Form of Siren
The Acoustical Shadow of a Circular Disk
[*Phil. Mag.* ix, pp. 278–283, 1880.]

*66. On the Stability, or Instability, of certain Fluid Motions
[*London Math. Soc. Proc.* xi, pp. 57–70, 1880.]

67. On the Resolving-Power of Telescopes
[*Phil. Mag.* x, pp. 116–119, 1880.]

68. On the Resultant of a large number of Vibrations of the same Pitch and of arbitrary Phase
[*Phil. Mag.* x, pp. 73–78, 1880.]

69. Note on the Theory of the Induction Balance
[*Brit. Assoc. Report*, Swansea, pp. 472, 473, 1880.]

70. On a New Arrangement for Sensitive Flames
[*Cambridge Phil. Soc. Proc.* iv, pp. 17, 18, 1880.]

71. The Photophone
[*Nature*, xxiii, pp. 274, 275, 1881.]

72. On Copying Diffraction-Gratings, and on some Phenomena connected therewith
[*Phil. Mag.* xi, pp. 196–205, 1881.]

84. Acoustical Observations. IV
   On the Pitch of Organ-Pipes
   Slow *versus* Quick Beats for comparison of Frequencies of Vibration
   Estimation of the Direction of Sounds with one Ear
   A Telephone-Experiment
   Very High Notes. Rapid Fatigue of the Ear
   Sensitive Flames
      [*Phil. Mag.* XIII, pp. 340–347, 1882.]

85. Further Observations upon Liquid Jets, in Continuation of those recorded in the Royal Society's 'Proceedings' for March and May, 1879
   On some of the Circumstances which influence the Scattering of a nearly Vertical Jet of Liquid
   Influence of Regular Vibrations of Low Pitch
   The Length of the Continuous Part
   Collision of Two Resolved Streams
   Collision of Streams before Resolution
      [*Proc. Roy. Soc.* XXXIV, pp. 130–145, 1882.]

*86. Address to the Mathematical and Physical Science Section of the British Association
      [*Brit. Assoc. Report*, pp. 437–441, 1882.]

87. On the Tension of Mercury Vapour at Common Temperatures
      [*Brit. Assoc. Report*, p. 441, 1882.]

88. On the Absolute Measurement of Electric Currents
      [*Brit. Assoc. Report*, pp. 445, 446, 1882.]

89. On the Duration of Free Electric Currents in an Infinite Conducting Cylinder
      [*Brit. Assoc. Report*, pp. 446, 447, 1882.]

90. On the Equilibrium of Liquid Conducting Masses charged with Electricity
      [*Phil. Mag.* XIV, pp. 184–186, 1882.]

*91. On an Instrument capable of Measuring the Intensity of Aerial Vibrations
      [*Phil. Mag.* XIV, pp. 186, 187, 1882.]

92. Comparison of Methods for the Determination of Resistances in Absolute Measure
      I. Kirchhoff's Method, Maxwell's *Electricity and Magnetism*, § 759
      II. Weber's Method by Transient Currents, Maxwell, § 760
      III. Method of Revolving Coil
      IV. Method of Foster and Lippmann
      V. Weber's Method by Damping
      VI. Lorenz's Method
         [*Phil. Mag.* XIV, pp. 329–346, 1882.]

93. On the Dark Plane which is formed over a Heated Wire in Dusty Air
      [*Proc. Roy. Soc.* XXXIV, pp. 414–418, 1882.]

94. Experiments, by the Method of Lorenz, for the Further Determination of the Absolute Value of the British Association Unit of Resistance, with an Appendix on the Determination of the Pitch of a Standard Tuning-Fork. By Lord Rayleigh and Mrs H. Sidgwick
    Details of Measurements:
        Diameter of Disc
        The Induction-Coils
        The Distance-Pieces
        The Induction-Coefficients
        The Resistance-Coils
    Appendix: Frequency of Vibration of Standard Fork
    Second Appendix: On the Effect of the Imperfect Insulation of Coils
        [*Phil. Trans.* CLXXIV, pp. 295–322, 1883.]

95. On the Mean Radius of Coils of Insulated Wire
        [*Cambridge Phil. Soc. Proc.* IV, pp. 321–324, 1883.]

96. On the Invisibility of Small Objects in a Bad Light
        [*Cambridge Phil. Soc. Proc.* IV, p. 4, 1883.]

97. On Maintained Vibrations
        [*Phil. Mag.* XV, pp. 229–235, 1883.]

98. The Soaring of Birds
        [*Nature*, XXVII, pp. 534, 535, 1883.]

99. Distribution of Energy in the Spectrum
        [*Nature*, XXVII, pp. 559, 560, 1883.]

100. Investigation of the Character of the Equilibrium of an Incompressible Heavy Fluid of Variable Density
        [*London Math. Soc. Proc.* XIV, pp. 170–177, 1883.]

101. On the Vibrations of a Cylindrical Vessel containing Liquid
        [*Phil. Mag.* XV, pp. 385–389, 1883.]

102. On the Crispations of Fluid resting upon a Vibrating Support
        [*Phil. Mag.* XVI, pp. 50–58, 1883.]

103. On Porous Bodies in Relation to Sound
        [*Phil. Mag.* XVI, pp. 181–186, 1883.]

104. Suggestions for Facilitating the Use of a Delicate Balance
        [*Brit. Assoc. Report*, pp. 401, 402, 1883.]

105. On the Imperfection of the Galvanometer as a Test of the Evanescence of a Transient Current
        [*Brit. Assoc. Report*, pp. 444, 445, 1883.]

106. On Laplace's Theory of Capillarity
        [*Phil. Mag.* XVI, pp. 309–315, 1883.]

107. On the Measurement of Electric Currents
        [*Cambridge Phil. Soc. Proc.* V, pp. 50–52, 1883.]

*108. On the Circulation of Air observed in Kundt's Tubes, and on some Allied Acoustical Problems
        [*Phil. Trans.* CLXXV, pp. 1–21, 1883.]

137. Notes, chiefly Historical, on some Fundamental Propositions in Optics
        [*Phil. Mag.* xxi, pp. 466–476, 1886.]

138. On the Intensity of Light Reflected from Certain Surfaces at Nearly
      Perpendicular Incidence
          Description of Apparatus
          Prism of Crown Glass (I)
          Prism of Crown Glass (II)
          Plate Glass Silvered Behind
          Silver-on-Glass Speculum
          Mirror of Black Glass
            [*Proc. Roy. Soc.* xli, pp. 275–294, 1886.]

139. Notes on Electricity and Magnetism. I. On the Energy of Magnetized
      Iron
            [*Phil. Mag.* xxii, pp. 175–183, 1886.]

140. Notes on Electricity and Magnetism. II. The Self-Induction and
      Resistance of Compound Conductors
          The Interrupters
          The Induction-Compensators
          Appendix.—The Induction-Compensators [p. 577]
            [*Phil. Mag.* xxii, pp. 469–500, 1886.]

141. Notes on Electricity and Magnetism. III. On the Behaviour of Iron
      and Steel under the Operation of Feeble Magnetic Forces
            [*Phil. Mag.* xxiii, pp. 225–245, 1887.]

142. On the Maintenance of Vibrations by Forces of Double Frequency,
      and on the Propagation of Waves through a Medium endowed with a
      Periodic Structure
            [*Phil. Mag.* xxiv, pp. 145–159, 1887.]

143. On the Existence of Reflection when the Relative Refractive Index is
      Unity
            [*Brit. Assoc. Report*, pp. 585, 586, 1887.]

144. On the Stability or Instability of Certain Fluid Motions, II
            [*London Math. Soc. Proc.* xix, pp. 67–74, 1887.]

145. Diffraction of Sound
            [*Roy. Inst. Proc.* xii, pp. 187–198, 1888; *Nature*, xxxviii, pp. 208–211, 1888.]

146. On the Relative Densities of Hydrogen and Oxygen. (Preliminary
      Notice)
            [*Proc. Roy. Soc.* xliii, pp. 356–363, 1888.]

147. On Point-, Line-, and Plane-Sources of Sound
            [*London Math. Soc. Proc.* xix, pp. 504–507, 1888.]

148. Wave Theory of Light
          Plane Waves of Simple Type
          Intensity
          Resultant of a Large Number of Vibrations of Arbitrary Phase
          Propagation of Waves in General

Waves Approximately Plane or Spherical
Interference Fringes
Colours of Thin Plates
Newton's Diffusion Rings
Huygens's Principle. Theory of Shadows
Fraunhofer's Diffraction Phenomena
Theory of Circular Aperture
Influence of Aberration. Optical Power of Instruments
Theory of Gratings
Theory of Corrugated Waves
Talbot's Bands
Diffraction when the Source of Light is not Seen in Focus
Diffraction Symmetrical about an Axis
Polarization
Interference of Polarized Light
Double Refraction
Colours of Crystalline Plates
Rotary Polarization
Dynamical Theory of Diffraction
The Diffraction of Light by Small Particles
Reflexion and Refraction
Reflexion on the Elastic Solid Theory
The Velocity of Light
[*Encyclopædia Britannica*, XXIV, 1888.]

149. On the Reflection of Light at a Twin Plane of a Crystal
Equations of a Dielectric Medium, of which the Magnetic Permeability is Unity throughout
Isotropic Reflexion
Propagation in a Crystal
Reflexion at a Twin Plane
Incidence in the Plane of Symmetry
Plane of Incidence perpendicular to that of Symmetry
Doubly Refracting Power Small
Plate bounded by Surfaces parallel to Twin Plane
[*Phil. Mag.* XXVI, pp. 241–255, 1888.]

150. On the Remarkable Phenomenon of Crystalline Reflexion described by Prof. Stokes
[*Phil. Mag.* XXVI, pp. 256–265, 1888.]

151. Is the Velocity of Light in an Electrolytic Liquid influenced by an Electric Current in the Direction of Propagation?
[*Brit. Assoc. Report*, pp. 341–343, 1888.].

152. On the Bending and Vibration of Thin Elastic Shells, especially of Cylindrical Form
[*Proc. Roy. Soc.* XLV, pp. 105–123, 1888.]

153. On the Composition of Water
[*Proc. Roy. Soc.* XLV, pp. 425–430, 1889.]

154. The History of the Doctrine of Radiant Energy
        [*Phil. Mag.* xxvii, pp. 265–270, 1889.]

155. Note on the Free Vibrations of an Infinitely Long Cylindrical Shell
        [*Proc. Roy. Soc.* xlv, pp. 443–448, 1889.]

156. On the Free Vibrations of an Infinite Plate of Homogeneous Isotropic
     Elastic Matter
        [*London Math. Soc. Proc.* xx, pp. 225–234, 1889.]

157. On the Limit to Interference when Light is Radiated from Moving
     Molecules
        [*Phil. Mag.* xxvii, pp. 298–304, 1889.]

158. Iridescent Crystals
        [*Proc. Roy. Inst.* xii, pp. 447–449, 1889; *Nature*, xl, pp. 227, 228, 1889.]

159. The Sailing Flight of the Albatross
        [*Nature*, xl, p. 34, 1889.]

160. On the Character of the Complete Radiation at a Given Temperature
        [*Phil. Mag.* xxvii, pp. 460–469, 1889.]

161. On the Visibility of Faint Interference-Bands
        [*Phil. Mag.* xxvii, pp. 484–486, 1889.]

162. On the Uniform Deformation in Two Dimensions of a Cylindrical
     Shell of Finite Thickness, with Application to the General Theory of
     Deformation of Thin Shells
        [*London Math. Soc. Proc.* xx, pp. 372–381, 1889.]

163. On Achromatic Interference-Bands
        Introduction
        Fresnel's Bands
        Lloyd's Bands
        Limit to Illumination
        Achromatic Interference-Bands
        Prism instead of Grating
        Airy's Theory of the White Centre
        Thin Plates
        Herschel's Bands
        Effect of a Prism upon Newton's Rings
        Analytical Statement
        Curved Interference-Bands
            [*Phil. Mag.* xxviii, pp. 77–91, 189–206, 1889.]

164. On Bells
        Appendix: On the Bending of a Hyperboloid of Revolution
            [*Phil. Mag.* xxix, pp. 1–17, 1890.]

165. The Clark Standard Cell
        [*The Electrician*, p. 285, Jan. 1890.]

166. On the Vibrations of an Atmosphere
        [*Phil. Mag.* xxix, pp. 173–180, 1890.]

Another Method of Investigation
Progress towards the Stationary State
Pendulums in place of Free Masses
[*Phil. Mag.* xxxii, pp. 424–445, 1891.]

184. Experiments in Aerodynamics. [Review of Langley's]
[*Nature*, xlv, pp. 108, 109, 1891.]

185. On Reflexion from Liquid Surfaces in the Neighbourhood of the Polarizing Angle
Postscript (October 11)
[*Phil. Mag.* xxxiii, pp. 1–19, Jan. 1892.]

186. On the Theory of Surface Forces. II. Compressible Fluids
[*Phil. Mag.* xxxiii, 209–220, 1892.]

187. On the Relative Densities of Hydrogen and Oxygen. II.
[*Proc. Roy. Soc.* l, pp. 448–463, 1892.]

188. Superheated Steam
Heat Engines and Saline Solutions
Heat Engines and Saline Solutions
[*Nature*, xlv, pp. 375, 376, 438, 512, 1892.]

189. Aberration
[*Nature*, xlv, pp. 499–502, 1892.]

190. Remarks on Maxwell's Investigation respecting Boltzmann's Theorem
[*Phil. Mag.* xxxiii, pp. 356–359, 1892.]

*191. On the Physics of Media that are composed of Free and Perfectly Elastic Molecules in a State of Motion. [Introduction to Waterston's Memoir]
[*Phil. Trans.* A, clxxxiii, pp. 1–5, 1892.]

192. Experiments upon Surface-Films
The Behaviour of Clean Mercury
Drops of Bisulphide of Carbon upon Water
Movements of Dust
Camphor Movements a Test of Surface-Tension
Influence of Heat
Saponine and Soap
Separation of Motes
The Lowering of Tension by the Condensation of Ether Vapour
Breath Figures and their Projection
[*Phil. Mag.* xxxiii, pp. 363–373, 1892.]

193. On the Theory of Surface Forces. III. Effect of Slight Contaminations
[*Phil. Mag.* xxxiii, pp. 468–471, 1892.]

194. On the Question of the Stability of the Flow of Fluids
[*Phil. Mag.* xxxiv, pp. 59–70, 1892.]

195. On the Instability of a Cylinder of Viscous Liquid under Capillary Force
[*Phil. Mag.* xxxiv, pp. 145–154, 1892.]

210.   On an Anomaly encountered in Determinations of the Density of Nitrogen Gas
         [*Proc. Roy. Soc.* LV, pp. 340–344, April, 1894.]

211.   On the Minimum Current audible in the Telephone
         [*Phil. Mag.* XXXVIII, pp. 285–295, 1894.]

212.   An Attempt at a Quantitative Theory of the Telephone
         [*Phil. Mag.* XXXVIII, pp. 295–301, 1894.]

213.   On the Amplitude of Aerial Waves which are but just Audible
         [*Phil. Mag.* XXXVIII, pp. 365–370, 1894.]

214.   Argon, a New Constituent of the Atmosphere. By LORD RAYLEIGH Sec. R.S., and PROFESSOR WILLIAM RAMSAY, F.R.S.
         1. Density of Nitrogen from Various Sources
         2. Reasons for Suspecting a hitherto Undiscovered Constituent in Air
         3. Methods of Causing Free Nitrogen to Combine
         4. Early Experiments on sparking Nitrogen with Oxygen in presence of Alkali
         5. Early Experiments on Withdrawal of Nitrogen from Air by means of Red-hot Magnesium
         6. Proof of the Presence of Argon in Air, by means of Atmolysis
         7. Negative Experiments to prove that Argon is not derived from Nitrogen or from Chemical Sources
         8. Separation of Argon on a Large Scale
         9. Density of Argon prepared by means of Oxygen
         10. Density of Argon prepared by means of Magnesium
         11. Spectrum of Argon
         12. Solubility of Argon in Water
         13. Behaviour at Low Temperatures
         14. The ratio of the Specific Heats of Argon
         15. Attempts to induce Chemical Combination
         16. General Conclusions
         Addendum, March 20 (by PROFESSOR W. RAMSAY)
         Addendum, April 9
           [*Phil. Trans.* A, pp. 187–241, 1895.]

*215.   Argon
         [*Proc. Roy. Inst.* XIV, pp. 524–538, April, 1895.]

216.   On the Stability or Instability of Certain Fluid Motions. III
         Addendum, January 1896
           [*London Math. Soc. Proc.* XXVII, pp. 5–12, 1895.]

217.   On the Propagation of Waves upon the Plane Surface separating Two Portions of Fluid of Different Vorticities
         [*London Math. Soc. Proc.* XXVII, pp. 13–18, 1895.]

218.   On Some Physical Properties of Argon and Helium
         Density of Argon
         The Refractivity of Argon and Helium
         Viscosity of Argon and Helium

230. On the Incidence of Aerial and Electric Waves upon Small Obstacles
    in the Form of Ellipsoids or Elliptic Cylinders, and on the passage of
    Electric Waves through a Circular Aperture in a Conducting Screen
      Obstacle in a Uniform Field
      In Two Dimensions
      Aerial Waves
      Waves in Two Dimensions
      Electrical Applications
      Electric Waves in Three Dimensions
      Obstacle in the Form of an Ellipsoid
      Circular Aperture in Conducting Screen
        [*Phil. Mag.* XLIV, pp. 28–52, 1897.]

231. On the Propagation of Electric Waves along Cylindrical Conductors
    of any Section
        [*Phil. Mag.* XLIV, pp. 199–204, 1897.]

232. The Electro-Chemical Equivalent of Silver
        [*Nature*, LVI, p. 292, 1897.]

233. On an Optical Device for the Intensification of Photographic Pictures
        [*Phil. Mag.* XLIV, pp. 282–285, 1897.]

234. On the Viscosity of Hydrogen as affected by Moisture
        [*Proc. Roy. Soc.* LXII, pp. 112–116, 1897.]

235. On the Propagation of Waves along Connected Systems of Similar
    Bodies
        [*Phil. Mag.* XLIV, pp. 356–362, 1897.]

236. On the Densities of Carbonic Oxide, Carbonic Anhydride, and
    Nitrous Oxide
      Carbonic Oxide
      Carbonic Anhydride
      Nitrous Oxide
        [*Proc. Roy. Soc.* LXII, pp. 204–209, 1897.]

237. Röntgen Rays and Ordinary Light
        [*Nature*, LVII, p. 607, 1898.]

238. Note on the Pressure of Radiation, showing an Apparent Failure of
    the Usual Electromagnetic Equations
        [*Phil. Mag.* XLV, pp. 522–525, 1898.]

239. Some Experiments with the Telephone
        [*Proc. Roy. Inst.* XV, pp. 786–789, 1898; *Nature*, LVIII, pp. 429–430, 1898.]

240. Liquid Air at one Operation
        [*Nature*, LVIII, p. 199, 1898.]

241. On the Character of the Impurity found in Nitrogen Gas Derived
    from Urea [with an Appendix containing details of Refractometer]
      Details of Refractometer
        [*Proc. Roy. Soc.* LXIV, pp. 95–100, 1898.]

242. On Iso-periodic Systems
        [*Phil. Mag.* XLVI, pp. 567–569, 1898.]

C

*260. Remarks upon the Law of Complete Radiation
      [*Phil. Mag.* XLIX, pp. 539, 540, 1900.]

261. On Approximately Simple Waves
      [*Phil. Mag.* L, pp. 135–139, 1900.]

262. On a Theorem analogous to the Virial Theorem
      [*Phil. Mag.* L, pp. 210–213, 1900.]

263. On Balfour Stewart's Theory of the Connexion between Radiation
      and Absorption
      [*Phil. Mag.* I, pp. 98–100, 1901.]

264. Spectroscopic Notes concerning the Gases of the Atmosphere
      On the Visibility of Hydrogen in Air
      Demonstration at Atmospheric Pressure of Argon from very small
      quantities of Air
      Concentration of Helium from the Atmosphere
      [*Phil. Mag.* I, pp. 100–105, 1901.]

265. On the Stresses in Solid Bodies due to Unequal Heating, and on the
      Double Refraction resulting therefrom
      [*Phil. Mag.* I, pp. 169–178, 1901.]

266. On a New Manometer, and on the Law of the Pressure of Gases
      between 1·5 and 0·01 Millimetres of Mercury
      Introduction
      Improved Apparatus for Measuring very small Pressures
      Experiments to determine the Relation of Pressure and Volume at
      given Temperature
      [*Phil. Trans.* CXCVI A, pp. 205–223, 1901.]

267. On a Problem relating to the Propagation of Sound between Parallel
      Walls
      [*Phil. Mag.* I, pp. 301–311, 1901.]

268. Polish
      [*Proc. Roy. Inst.* XVI, pp. 563–570, 1901; *Nature*, LXIV, pp. 385–388, 1901.]

269. Does Chemical Transformation influence Weight?
      [*Nature*, LXIV, p. 181, June, 1901.]

270. Acoustical Notes. VI
      Forced Vibrations
      Vibrations of Strings
      Beats of Sounds led to the Two Ears separately
      Loudness of Double Sounds
      [*Phil. Mag.* II, pp. 280–285, 1901.]

271. On the Magnetic Rotation of Light and the Second Law of Thermo-
      dynamics
      [*Nature*, LXIV, pp. 577, 578, 1901.]

272. On the Induction-Coil
      [*Phil. Mag.* II, pp. 581–594, 1901.]

273. Interference of Sound
      [*Proc. Roy. Inst.* XVII, pp. 1–7, 1902; *Nature*, LXVI, pp. 42–44, 1902.]

282. Note on the Theory of the Fortnightly Tide
     [*Phil. Mag.* v, pp. 136–141, 1903.]

283. On the Free Vibrations of Systems affected with Small Rotatory Terms
     [*Phil. Mag.* v, pp. 293–297, 1903.]

284. On the Vibrations of a Rectangular Sheet of Rotating Liquid
     [*Phil. Mag.* v, pp. 297–301, 1903.]

285. On the Spectrum of an Irregular Disturbance
     [*Phil. Mag.* v, pp. 238–243, 1903.]

286. Considerations respecting the Combustion of Modern Propellants in Closed Vessels and in Guns
     Closed Vessels
     Combustion in Guns
     [*Minutes of Explosives Committee*, 1903.]

287. On the Bending of Waves round a Spherical Obstacle
     [*Proc. Roy. Soc.* LXXII, pp. 40–41, 1903.]

288. On the Proportion of Argon in the Vapour rising from Liquid Air
     [*Phil. Mag.* v, pp. 677–680, 1903.]

289. On the Theory of Optical Images, with Special Reference to the Microscope. (Supplementary Paper)
     [*Journ. R. Micr. Soc.* pp. 474–482, 1903.]

290. On the Production and Distribution of Sound
     Theory of Conical Trumpet
     Data respecting Fog-Signals
     Comparison with Musical Instruments, &c.
     Cones and Resonators
     Vibration Indicator
     Reeds
     Trumpets of Elongated Section
     Work done by Detached Sources
     Continuous Distributions
     Experimental Illustrations
     [*Phil. Mag.* VI, pp. 289–305, 1903.]

291. On the Work done by Forces operative at one or more Points of an Elastic Solid
     [*Phil. Mag.* VI, pp. 385–392, 1903.]

292. On the Acoustic Shadow of a Sphere
     Appendix. By Professor A. LODGE
     Note by LORD RAYLEIGH
     [*Phil. Trans.* A, CCIII, pp. 87–110, 1904.]

293. Shadows
     [*Proc. Roy. Inst.* Jan. 15, 1904.]

294. Sir George Gabriel Stokes, Bart., 1819–1903
     [*Royal Society Year-Book*, 1904.]

309. On the Momentum and Pressure of Gaseous Vibrations, and on the Connexion with the Virial Theorem
     [*Phil. Mag.* x, pp. 364–374, 1905.]

310. The Origin of the Prismatic Colours
     [*Phil. Mag.* x, pp. 401–407, 1905.]

311. On the Constitution of Natural Radiation
     [*Phil. Mag.* xi, pp. 123–127, 1906.]

312. On an Instrument for compounding Vibrations, with Application to the drawing of Curves such as might represent White Light
     Note on the Principle of the Sand-Clock
     [*Phil. Mag.* xi, pp. 127–130, 1906.]

*313. On Electrical Vibrations and the Constitution of the Atom
     [*Phil. Mag.* xi, pp. 117–123, 1906.]

314. On the Production of Vibrations by Forces of Relatively Long Duration, with Application to the Theory of Collisions
     [*Phil. Mag.* xi, pp. 283–291, 1906.]

315. On the Dilatational Stability of the Earth
     [*Proc. Roy. Soc.* A, lxxvii, pp. 486–499, 1906.]

316. Some Measurements of Wave-Lengths with a Modified Apparatus
     [*Phil. Mag.* xi, pp. 685–703, 1906.]

317. On the Experimental Determination of the Ratio of the Electrical Units
     [*Phil. Mag.* xii, pp. 97–108, 1906.]

318. On the Interference-Rings, described by Haidinger, observable by means of Plates whose Surfaces are absolutely Parallel
     [*Phil. Mag.* xii, pp. 489–493, 1906.]

319. On our Perception of Sound Direction
     [*Phil. Mag.* xiii, pp. 214–232, 1907.]

320. Acoustical Notes. VII
     Sensations of Right and Left from a revolving Magnet and Tele-phones
     Multiple Harmonic Resonator
     Tuning-Forks with slight Mutual Influence
     Mutual Reaction of Singing Flames
     Longitudinal Balance of Tuning-Forks
     A Tuning-Fork Siren and its Maintenance
     Stroboscopic Speed Regulation
     Phonic Wheel and Commutator
     [*Phil. Mag.* xiii, pp. 316–333, 1907.]

321. On the Passage of Sound through Narrow Slits
     Appendix
     [*Phil. Mag.* xiv, pp. 153–161, 1907.]

322. On the Dynamical Theory of Gratings
     [*Proc. Roy. Soc.* A, lxxix, pp. 399–416, 1907.]

335. On the Instantaneous Propagation of Disturbance in a Dispersive
      Medium, exemplified by Waves on Water Deep and Shallow
            [*Phil. Mag.* XVIII, pp. 1–6, 1909.]

336. On the Resistance due to Obliquely Moving Waves and its Depen-
      dence upon the Particular Form of the Fore-part of a Ship
            [*Phil. Mag.* XVIII, pp. 414–416, 1909.]

337. On the Perception of the Direction of Sound
            [*Proc. Roy. Soc.* A, LXXXIII, pp. 61–64, 1909.]

338. The Theory of Crookes's Radiometer
            [*Nature*, LXXXI, pp. 69, 70, 1909.]

339. To determine the Refractivity of Gases available only in Minute
      Quantities
            [*Nature*, LXXXI, p. 519, 1909.]

*340. Note as to the Application of the Principle of Dynamical Similarity
            [*Report of the Advisory Committee for Aeronautics*, p. 38, 1909—10.]

341. The Principle of Dynamical Similarity in Reference to the Results of
      Experiments on the Resistance of Square Plates Normal to a Current
      of Air
            [*Report of Advisory Committee*, 1910-11.]

342. Note on the Regularity of Structure of Actual Crystals
            [*Phil. Mag.* XIX, pp. 96–99, 1910.]

343. Colours of Sea and Sky
            [*Proc. Roy. Inst.* Feb. 25, 1910; *Nature*, LXXXIII, p. 48, 1910.]

344. The Incidence of Light upon a Transparent Sphere of Dimensions
      comparable with the Wave-Length
          Experimental
            [*Proc. Roy. Soc.* A, LXXXIV, pp. 25–46, 1910.]

345. On Colour Vision at the ends of the Spectrum
            [*Nature*, LXXXIV, pp. 204, 205, 1910.]

346. Aerial Plane Waves of Finite Amplitude
          Waves of Finite Amplitude without Dissipation
          Waves of Permanent Regime
          Permanent Regime under the influence of Dissipative Forces
          Resistance to Motion through Air at High Velocities
            [*Proc. Roy. Soc.* A, LXXXIV, pp. 247–284, 1910.]

347. Note on the Finite Vibrations of a System about a Configuration of
      Equilibrium
            [*Phil. Mag.* XX, pp. 450–456, 1910.]

348. The Problem of the Whispering Gallery
            [*Phil. Mag.* XX, pp. 1001–1004, 1910.]

349. On the Sensibility of the Eye to Variations of Wave-Length in the
      Yellow Region of the Spectrum
            [*Proc. Roy. Soc.* A, LXXXV, pp. 464–468, 1910.]

C*

366. Coloured Photometry
        [*Phil. Mag.* xxiv, pp. 301, 302, 1912.]

367. On some Iridescent Films
        [*Phil. Mag.* xxiv, pp. 751–755, 1912.]

368. Breath Figures
        [*Nature*, xc, pp. 436, 437, 1912.]

369. Remarks concerning Fourier's Theorem as applied to Physical Problems
        [*Phil. Mag.* xxiv, pp. 864–869, 1912.]

370. Sur la Resistance des Sphères dans l'Air en Mouvement
        [*Comptes Rendus*, t. clvi, p. 109, 1913.]

371. The Effect of Junctions on the Propagation of Electric Waves along Conductors
        [*Proc. Roy. Soc.* A, lxxxviii, pp. 103–110, 1913.]

372. The Correction to the Length of Terminated Rods in Electrical Problems
        [*Phil. Mag.* xxv, pp. 1–9, 1913.]

373. On Conformal Representation from a Mechanical Point of View
        [*Phil. Mag.* xxv, pp. 698–702, 1913.]

374. On the Approximate Solution of Certain Problems relating to the Potential. II
        [*Phil. Mag.* xxvi, pp. 195–199, 1913.]

375. On the Passage of Waves through Fine Slits in Thin Opaque Screens
        [*Proc. Roy. Soc.* A, lxxxix, pp. 194–219, 1913.]

376. On the Motion of a Viscous Fluid
        [*Phil. Mag.* xxvi, pp. 776–786, 1913.]

377. On the Stability of the Laminar Motion of an Inviscid Fluid
        [*Phil. Mag.* xxvi, pp. 1001–1010, 1913.]

378. Reflection of Light at the Confines of a Diffusing Medium
        [*Nature*, xcii, p. 450, 1913.]

*379. The Pressure of Radiation and Carnot's Principle
        [*Nature*, xcii, pp. 527, 528, 1914.]

380. Further Applications of Bessel's Functions of High Order to the Whispering Gallery and Allied Problems
        [*Phil. Mag.* xxvii, pp. 100–109, 1914.]

381. On the Diffraction of Light by Spheres of Small Relative Index
        [*Proc. Roy. Soc.* A, xc, pp. 219–225, 1914.]

382. Some Calculations in Illustration of Fourier's Theorem
        [*Proc. Roy. Soc.* A, xc, pp. 318–323, 1914.]

383. Further Calculations concerning the Momentum of Progressive Waves
        [*Phil. Mag.* xxvii, pp. 436–440, 1914.]

384. Fluid Motions
        [*Proc. Roy. Inst.* March, 1914; *Nature*, xciii, p. 364, 1914.]

403. On the Electrical Capacity of Approximate Spheres and Cylinders
[*Phil. Mag.* xxxi, pp. 177–186, 1916.]

404. On Legendre's Function $P_n(\theta)$, when n is great and θ has any value†
[*Proc. Roy. Soc.* A, xcii, pp. 433–437, 1916.]

405. Memorandum on Fog Signals
[*Report to Trinity House*, May 1916.]

406. Lamb's *Hydrodynamics*
[*Nature*, xcvii, p. 318, 1916.]

407. On the Flow of Compressible Fluid past an Obstacle
[*Phil. Mag.* xxxii, pp. 1–6, 1916.]

408. On the Discharge of Gases under High Pressures
[*Phil. Mag.* xxxii, pp. 177–187, 1916.]

409. On the Energy acquired by Small Resonators from Incident Waves of like Period
[*Phil. Mag.* xxxii, pp. 188–190, 1916.]

410. On the Attenuation of Sound in the Atmosphere
[*Advisory Committee for Aeronautics*, Aug. 1916.]

411. On Vibrations and Deflexions of Membranes, Bars, and Plates
[*Phil. Mag.* xxxii, pp. 353–364, 1916.]

412. On Convection Currents in a Horizontal Layer of Fluid, when the Higher Temperature is on the Under Side
Appendix
[*Phil. Mag.* xxxii, pp 529–546, 1916.]

413. On the Dynamics of Revolving Fluids
[*Proc. Roy. Soc.* A, xciii, pp. 148–154, 1916.]

414. Propagation of Sound in Water
First published in the Dover edition of Rayleigh's *Scientific Papers* 1964.

415. On Methods for Detecting Small Optical Retardations, and on the Theory of Foucault's Test
[*Phil. Mag.* xxxiii, pp. 161–178, 1917.]

416. Talbot's Observations on Fused Nitre
[*Nature*, xcviii, p. 428, 1917.]

417. Cutting and Chipping of Glass
[*Engineering*, p. 111. Feb. 2, 1917,]

418. The Le Chatelier-Braun Principle
[*Trans. Chem. Soc.* cxi, pp. 250–252, 1917.]

419. On Periodic Irrotational Waves at the Surface of Deep Water
[*Phil. Mag.* xxxiii, pp. 381–389, 1917.]

420. On the Suggested Analogy between the Conduction of Heat and Momentum during the Turbulent Motion of a Fluid
[*Advisory Committee for Aeronautics*, T. 941, 1917.]

† [1917. It would be more correct to say $P_n(\cos\theta)$, where $\cos\theta$ lies between ± 1.]

421. The Theory of Anomalous Dispersion
     [*Phil. Mag.* xxxiii, pp. 496–499, 1917.]

422. On the Reflection of Light from a regularly Stratified Medium
     [*Proc. Roy. Soc.* A, xciii, pp. 565–577, 1917.]

*423. On the Pressure developed in a Liquid during the Collapse of a Spherical Cavity
      [*Phil. Mag.* xxxiv, pp. 94–98, 1917.]

424. On the Colours Diffusely Reflected from some Collodion Films spread on Metal Surfaces
     [*Phil. Mag.* xxxiv, pp. 423–428, 1917.]

425. Memorandum on Synchronous Signalling
     [*Report to Trinity House*, 1917.]

426. A Simple Problem in Forced Lubrication
     [*Engineering*, Dec. 14, 28, 1917.]

427. On the Scattering of Light by Spherical Shells, and by Complete Spheres of Periodic Structure, when the Refractivity is Small
     [*Proc. Roy. Soc.* A, xciv, pp. 296–300, 1918.]

428. Notes on the Theory of Lubrication
     [*Phil. Mag.* xxxv, pp. 1–12, 1918.]

429. On the Lubricating and other Properties of Thin Oily Films
     [*Phil. Mag.* xxxv, pp. 157–162, 1918.]

430. On the Scattering of Light by a Cloud of Similar Small Particles of any Shape and Oriented at Random
     [*Phil. Mag.* xxxv, pp. 373–381, 1918.]

431. Propagation of Sound and Light in an Irregular Atmosphere
     [*Nature*, ci, p. 284, 1918.]

432. Note on the Theory of the Double Resonator
     [*Phil. Mag.* xxxvi, pp. 231–234, 1918.]

433. A Proposed Hydraulic Experiment
     [*Phil. Mag.* xxxvi, pp. 315, 316, 1918.]

434. On the Dispersal of Light by a Dielectric Cylinder
     [*Phil. Mag.* xxxvi, pp. 365–376, 1918.]

435. The Perception of Sound
     [*Nature*, cii, 225, 1918.]

436. On the Light Emitted from a Random Distribution of Luminous Sources
     [*Phil. Mag.* xxxvi, pp. 429–449, 1918.]

437. The Perception of Sound
     [*Nature*, cii, 304, 1918.]

438. On the Optical Character of some Brilliant Animal Colours
     [*Phil. Mag.* xxxvii, pp. 98–111, 1919.]

439. On the Possible Disturbance of a Range-Finder by Atmospheric Refraction due to the Motion of the Ship which carries it
[*Trans. Optical Soc.* xx, pp. 125–129, 1919.]

440. Remarks on Major G. I. Taylor's Papers on the Distribution of Air Pressure
[*Advisory Committee for Aeronautics*, T. 1296, 1919.]

441. On the Problem of Random Vibrations, and of Random Flights in One, Two, or Three Dimensions
One Dimension
Two Dimensions
Three Dimensions
[*Phil. Mag.* xxxvii, pp. 321–347, 1919.

442. On the Resultant of a Number of Unit Vibrations, whose Phases are at Random over a Range not Limited to an Integral Number of Periods
[*Phil. Mag.* xxvii, pp. 498–515, 1919.]

*443. Presidential Address
[*Proc. Soc. Psychical Research*, xxx, pp. 275–290, 1919.]

444. The Travelling Cyclone
[*Phil. Mag.* xxxviii, pp. 420–424, 1919.]

445. Periodic Precipitates
Hookham's Crystals
[*Phil. Mag.* xxxviii, pp. 738–740, 1919.]

446. On Resonant Reflexion of Sound from a Perforated Wall
[*Phil. Mag.* xxxix, pp. 225–233, 1920.]

PART III

SELECTIONS FROM
RAYLEIGH'S SCIENTIFIC PAPERS

On the Theory of Resonance (1870)

[*Philosophical Transactions*. CLXI, pp. 77–118; read Nov. 1870.*]

Editorial Preface

This was Rayleigh's first paper on acoustics. It was based on a study of Helmholtz's elaborate studies of the famous resonators long known by his name. Rayleigh attempted with success to simplify and generalize Helmholtz's treatment. The general line of attack is well set out in his introduction. In this paper there is introduced the important concept of acoustic conductivity. It will be observed that though the author fully justifies the assignment of this term to the quantity *c* which he introduces in his analysis, he does not actually employ it here, as he did later in his *Theory of Sound*, in which much of the present treatment is presented in revised form.

Introduction

Although the theory of aerial vibrations has been treated by more than one generation of mathematicians and experimenters, comparatively little has been done towards a clear view of what goes on in any but the more simple cases. The extreme difficulty of anything like a general deductive investigation of the question is no doubt one reason. On the other hand, experimenters on this, as on other subjects, have too often observed and measured blindly without taking sufficient care to simplify the conditions of their experiments, so as to attack as few difficulties as possible at a time. The result has been vast accumulations of isolated facts and measurements which lie as a sort of dead weight on the scientific stomach, and which must remain undigested until theory supplies a more powerful solvent than any now at our command. The motion of the air in cylindrical organ-pipes was successfully investigated by Bernoulli and Euler, at least in its main features;

* Additions made since the paper was first sent to the Royal Society are inclosed in square brackets [ ].

but their treatment of the question of the open pipe was incomplete, or even erroneous, on account of the assumption that at the open end the air remains of invariable density during the vibration. Although attacked by many others, this difficulty was not finally overcome until Helmholtz*, in a paper which I shall have repeated occasion to refer to, gave a solution of the problem under certain restrictions, free from any arbitrary assumptions as to what takes place at the open end. Poisson and Stokes† have solved the problem of the vibrations communicated to an infinite mass of air from the surface of a sphere or circular cylinder. The solution for the sphere is very instructive, because the vibrations outside any imaginary sphere enclosing vibrating bodies of any kind may be supposed to take their rise in the surface of the sphere itself.

More important in its relation to the subject of the present paper is an investigation by Helmholtz of the air-vibrations in cavernous spaces (*Hohlraüme*), whose three dimensions are very small compared to the wavelength, and which communicate with the external atmosphere by small holes in their surfaces. If the opening be circular of area σ, and if S denote the volume, n the number of vibrations per second in the fundamental note, and a the velocity of sound,

$$n = \frac{a\sigma^{\frac{1}{2}}}{2^{\frac{1}{2}}\pi^{\frac{3}{4}}S^{\frac{1}{2}}}.$$

Helmholtz's theory is also applicable when there are more openings than one in the side of the vessel.

In the present paper I have attempted to give the theory of vibrations of this sort in a more general form. The extension to the case where the communication with the external air is no longer by a mere hole in the side, but by a neck of greater or less length, is important, not only because resonators with necks are frequently used in practice, but also by reason of the fact that the theory itself is applicable within wider limits. The mathematical reasoning is very different from that of Helmholtz, at least in form, and will I hope be found easier. In order to assist those who

* Theorie der Luftschwingungen in Röhren mit offenen Enden. *Crelle*, 1860.
† *Phil. Trans.* 1868, or *Phil. Mag.* Dec. 1868.

may wish only for clear general ideas on the subject, I have broken up the investigation as much as possible into distinct problems, the results of which may in many cases be taken for granted without the rest becoming unintelligible. In Part I. my object has been to put what may be called the dynamical part of the subject in a clear light, deferring as much as possible special mathematical calculations. In the first place, I have considered the general theory of resonance for air-spaces confined nearly all round by rigid walls, and communicating with the external air by any number of passages which may be of the nature of necks or merely holes, under the limitation that both the length of the necks and the dimensions of the vessel are very small compared to the wave-length. To prevent misapprehension, I ought to say that the theory applies only to the fundamental note of the resonators, for the vibrations corresponding to the overtones are of an altogether different character. There are, however, cases of multiple resonance to which our theory is applicable. These occur when two or more vessels communicate with each other and with the external air by necks or otherwise; and are easily treated by Lagrange's general dynamical method, subject to a restriction as to the relative magnitudes of the wave-lengths and the dimensions of the system corresponding to that stated above for a single vessel. I am not aware whether this kind of resonance has been investigated before, either mathematically or experimentally. Lastly, I have sketched a solution of the problem of the open organ-pipe on the same general plan, which may be acceptable to those who are not acquainted with Helmholtz's most valuable paper. The method here adopted, though it leads to results essentially the same as his, is I think more calculated to give an insight into the real nature of the question, and at the same time presents fewer mathematical difficulties. For a discussion of the solution, however, I must refer to Helmholtz.

In Part II. the calculation of a certain quantity depending on the form of the necks of common resonators, and involved in the results of Part I., is entered upon. This quantity, denoted by c, is of the nature of a length, and is identical with what would be called in the theory of electricity the *electric conductivity* of the passage, supposed to be occupied by uniformly conducting matter. The question is accordingly similar to that of determining the electrical resistance of variously shaped conductors— an analogy of which I have not hesitated to avail myself freely both in investigation and statement. Much circumlocution is in this way avoided on account of the greater completeness of electrical phraseology. Passing over the case of mere holes, which has been already considered by Helmholtz, and need not be dwelt upon here, we come to the value of the resistance for necks in the form of circular cylinders. For the sake of simplicity each end is supposed to be in an infinite plane. In this form the mathematical problem is definite, but has not been solved rigorously. Two limits, however (a higher and a lower), are investigated, between which it is proved that the true resistance must lie. The lower corresponds to a correction to the length of the tube equal to $\frac{1}{4}\pi \times$ (radius) for each end. It is a remarkable coincidence that Helmholtz also finds the same quantity as an approximate correction to the length of an organ-pipe, although the two methods are entirely different and neither of them rigorous. His consists of an exact solution of the problem for an approximate cylinder, and mine of an approximate solution for a true cylinder; while both indicate on which side the truth must lie. The final result for a cylinder infinitely long is that the correction lies between $\cdot785\,R$ and $\cdot828\,R$. When the cylinder is finite, the upper limit is rather smaller. In a somewhat similar manner I have investigated limits for the resistance of a tube of revolution, which is shown to lie between

$$\int \frac{dx}{\pi y^2} \quad \text{and} \quad \int \frac{dx}{\pi y^2} \left\{ 1 + \tfrac{1}{2} \left(\frac{dy}{dx} \right)^2 \right\},$$

where y denotes the radius of the tube at any point x along the axis. These formulae apply whatever may be in other respects the form of the tube, but are especially valuable when it is so nearly cylindrical that dy/dx is everywhere small. The two limits are then very near each other, and either of them gives very approximately the true value. The resistance of tubes, which are either not of revolution or are not nearly straight, is afterwards approximately determined. The only experimental results bearing on the subject of this paper, and available for comparison with theory, that I have met with are some arrived at by Sondhauss* and Wertheim†. Besides those quoted by Helmholtz, I have only to mention a series of observations by Sondhauss‡ on the pitch of flasks with long necks which led him to the empirical formula

$$n = 46705 \frac{\sigma^{\frac{1}{2}}}{L^{\frac{1}{2}} S^{\frac{1}{2}}},$$

σ, L being the area and length of the neck, and S the volume of the flask. The corresponding equation derived from the theory of the present paper is

$$n = 54470 \frac{\sigma^{\frac{1}{2}}}{L^{\frac{1}{2}} S^{\frac{1}{2}}},$$

which is only applicable, however, when the necks are so long that the corrections at the ends may be neglected—a condition not likely to be fulfilled. This consideration sufficiently explains the discordance. Being anxious to give the formulae of Parts I. and II. a fair trial, I investigated experimentally the resonance of a considerable number of vessels which were of such a form that the theoretical pitch could be calculated with tolerable accuracy. The result of the comparison is detailed in Part III., and appears on the whole very satisfactory; but it is not necessary that I should describe it more minutely here. I will only mention, as perhaps a novelty, that the experimental determination of the pitch was not made by causing the resonators to speak by a stream of air blown over their mouths. The grounds of my dissatisfaction with this method are explained in the proper place.

[Since this paper was written there has appeared another

* Pogg. *Ann.* vol. LXXXI.
† *Annales de Chimie*, vol. XXXI.
‡ Pogg. *Ann.* vol. LXXIX.

memoir by Dr Sondhauss* on the subject of resonance. An empirical formula is obtained bearing resemblance to the results of Parts I. and II., and agreeing fairly well with observation. No attempt is made to connect it with the fundamental principles of mechanics. In the *Philosophical Magazine* for September 1870 I have discussed the differences between Dr Sondhauss's formula and my own from the experimental side, and shall not therefore go any further into the matter on the present occasion.]

Part I

The class of resonators to which attention will chiefly be given in this paper are those where a mass of air confined almost all round by rigid walls communicates with the external atmosphere by one or more narrow passages. For the present it may be supposed that the boundary of the principal mass of air is part of an oval surface, nowhere contracted into anything like a narrow neck, although some cases not coming under this description will be considered later. In its general character the fundamental vibration of such an air-space is sufficiently simple, consisting of a periodical rush of air through the narrow channel (if there is only one) into and out of the confined space, which acts the part of a reservoir. The channel spoken of may be either a mere hole of any shape in the side of the vessel, or may consist of a more or less elongated tube-like passage.

If the linear dimension of the reservoir be small as compared to the wave-length of the vibration considered, or, as perhaps it ought rather to be said, the quarter wave-length, the motion is remarkably amenable to deductive treatment. Vibration in general may be considered as a periodic transformation of energy from the potential to the kinetic, and from the kinetic to the potential forms. In our case the kinetic energy is that of the air in the neighbourhood of the opening as it rushes backwards or forwards. It may be easily seen that relatively to this the energy

Pogg. *Ann.* 1870.

of the motion inside the reservoir is, under the restriction specified, very small. A formal proof would require the assistance of the general equations to the motion of an elastic fluid, whose use I wish to avoid in this paper. Moreover the motion in the passage and its neighbourhood will not differ sensibly from that of an incompressible fluid, and its energy will depend only on the rate of total flow through the opening. A quarter of a period later this energy of motion will be completely converted into the potential energy of the compressed or rarefied air inside the reservoir. So soon as the mathematical expressions for the potential and kinetic energies are known, the determination of the period of vibration or resonant note of the air-space presents no difficulty.

The motion of an incompressible frictionless fluid which has been once at rest is subject to the same formal laws as those which regulate the flow of heat or electricity through uniform conductors, and depends on the properties of the potential function, to which so much attention has of late years been given. In consequence of this analogy many of the results obtained in this paper are of as much interest in the theory of electricity as in acoustics, while, on the other hand, known modes of expression in the former subject will save circumlocution in stating some of the results of the present problem.

Let h_0 be the density, and ϕ the velocity-potential of the fluid motion through an opening. The kinetic energy or *vis viva*

$$= \tfrac{1}{2}h_0 \iiint \left[\left(\frac{d\phi}{dx} \right)^2 + \left(\frac{d\phi}{dy} \right)^2 + \left(\frac{d\phi}{dz} \right)^2 \, dx \, dy \, dz, \right.$$

the integration extending over the volume of the fluid considered

$$= \tfrac{1}{2}h_0 \iint \phi \frac{d\phi}{dn} \, dS, \quad \text{by Green's theorem.}$$

Over the rigid boundary of the opening or passage, $d\phi/dn = 0$, so that if the portion of fluid considered be bounded by two equipotential surfaces, ϕ_1 and ϕ_2, one on each side of the opening,

$$vis\ viva = \tfrac{1}{2}h_0\,(\phi_1 - \phi_2)\iint\frac{d\phi}{dn}\,dS = \tfrac{1}{2}h_0\,(\phi_1 - \phi_2)\,\dot{X},$$

if $\dot{X}$ denote the rate of total flow through the opening.

At a sufficient distance on either side ϕ becomes constant, and the rate of total flow is proportional to the difference of its values on the two sides. We may therefore put

$$\phi_1 - \phi_2 = \frac{1}{c}\iint\frac{d\phi}{dn}\,dS = \frac{\dot{X}}{c}\,,$$

where c is a linear quantity depending on the size and shape of the opening, and representing in the electrical interpretation the reciprocal of the *resistance* to the passage of electricity through the space in question, the specific resistance of the conducting matter being taken for unity. The same thing may be otherwise expressed by saying that c is the side of a cube, whose resistance between faces is the same as that of the opening.

The expression for the *vis viva* in terms of the rate of total flow is accordingly

$$vis\ viva = \frac{h_0}{2}\frac{\dot{X}^2}{c}\,. \tag{1}$$

If S be the capacity of the reservoir, the condensation at any time inside it is given by X/S, of which the mechanical value is

$$\tfrac{1}{2}h_0a^2\frac{X^2}{S}\,, \tag{2}$$

a denoting, as throughout the paper, the velocity of sound.

The whole energy at any time, both actual and potential, is therefore

$$\frac{h_0}{2}\frac{\dot{X}^2}{c} + \frac{h_0}{2}a^2\frac{X^2}{S}\,, \tag{3}$$

and is constant. Differentiating with respect to time, we arrive at

$$X + \frac{a^2c}{S}X = 0 \tag{4}$$

as the equation to the motion, which indicates simple oscillations performed in a time

$$2\pi \div \sqrt{\left(\frac{a^2c}{S}\right)}.$$

Hence if n denote the number of vibrations per second in the resonant note,

$$n = \frac{a}{2\pi} \sqrt{\left(\frac{c}{S}\right)}. \qquad (5)$$

The wave-length λ, which is the quantity most immediately connected with the dimensions of the resonant space, is given by

$$\lambda = \frac{a}{n} = 2\pi \sqrt{\left(\frac{S}{c}\right)}. \qquad (6)$$

A law of Savart, not nearly so well known as it ought to be, is in agreement with equations (5) and (6). It is an immediate consequence of the principle of dynamical similarity, of extreme generality, to the effect that *similar* vibrating bodies, whether they be gaseous, such as the air in organ-pipes or in the resonators here considered, or solid, such as tuning-forks, vibrate in a time which is directly as their linear dimensions. Of course the material must be the same in two cases that are to be compared, and the geometrical similarity must be complete, extending to the shape of the opening as well as to the other parts of the resonant vessel. Although the wave-length λ is a function of the size and shape of the resonator only, n or the position of the note in the musical scale depends on the nature of the gas with which the resonator is filled. And it is important to notice that it is on the nature of the gas in and near the opening that the note depends, and *not* on the gas in the interior of the reservoir, whose inertia does not come into play during vibrations corresponding to the fundamental note. In fact we may say that the mass to be moved is the air in the neighbourhood of the opening, and that the air in the interior acts merely as a spring in virtue of its resistance to compression. Of course this is only true under the limitation specified, that the diameter of the reservoir is small compared to the quarter wavelength. Whether this condition is fulfilled in the case of any particular resonator is easily seen, *à posteriori*, by calculating the value of λ from (6), or by determining it experimentally.

Editorial comment

In the remainder of the article after this extract from its beginning, the author undertakes the calculation of the acoustic conductivity for various kinds of orifices, evaluates the well-known end correction to a tube or organ pipe, and discusses such special cases as coupled resonators. He concludes the paper with an account of some experimental studies of his own resonators yielding good agreement with his theoretical results.

On the Light from the Sky, its Polarization and Colour (1871)

[*Philosophical Magazine.* XLI, pp. 107–120, 274–279; 1871]

Editorial Preface

This is one of Rayleigh's most celebrated papers and marks the beginning of his concern for radiation scattering in general. The reader will note the skilful way in which the author arrives at both the intensity and polarization of the scattered light by the use of dimensional considerations with a minimum of analysis. Here Rayleigh indulges in a method he often used in subsequent work. An outline of the actual wave theory analysis is given leading to the same result as the previous general physical considerations. This is indeed based on a more detailed analysis presented in an appendix to the complete paper, but not reproduced here.

It is now, I believe, generally admitted that the light which we receive from the clear sky is due in one way or another to small suspended particles which divert the light from its regular course. On this point the experiments of Tyndall with precipitated clouds seem quite decisive. Whenever the particles of the foreign matter are sufficiently fine, the light emitted laterally is blue in colour, and, in a direction perpendicular to that of the incident beam, is *completely polarized*.

About the colour there is no *prima facie* difficulty; for as soon as the question is raised, it is seen that the standard of linear dimension, with reference to which the particles are called small, is the wave-length of light, and that a given set of particles would (on any conceivable view as to their mode of action) produce a continually increasing disturbance as we pass along the spectrum towards the more refrangible end; and there seems no reason why the colour of the compound light thus scattered laterally should not agree with that of the sky.

On the other hand, the direction of polarization (perpendicular to the path of the primary light) seems to have been felt as a difficulty. Tyndall says, ". . . the polarization of the beam by the incipient cloud has thus far proved itself to be *absolutely independent of the polarizing-angle.* The law of Brewster does not apply to matter in this condition; and it rests with the undulatory theory to explain why. Whenever the precipitated particles are sufficiently fine, no matter what the substance forming the particles may be, the direction of maximum polarization is at right angles to the illuminating beam, the polarizing angle for matter in this condition being invariably 45°. This I consider to be a point of capital importance with reference to the present question"*. As to the importance there will not be two opinions; but I venture to think that the difficulty is imaginary, and is caused mainly by misuse of the word reflection. Of course there is nothing in the etymology of reflection or refraction to forbid their application in this sense; but the words have acquired technical meanings, and become associated with certain well-known laws called after them. Now a moment's consideration of the principles according to which reflection and refraction are explained in the wave theory is sufficient to show that they have no application unless the surface of the disturbing body is larger than many square wave-lengths; whereas the particles to which the sky is supposed to owe its illumination must be *smaller* than the wave-length, or else the explanation of the colour breaks down. The idea of polarization by reflection is therefore out of place; and that "the law of Brewster does not apply to matter in this condition" (of extreme fineness) is only what might have been inferred from the principles of the wave theory.

Nor is there any difficulty in foreseeing what, according to the wave theory, the direction of polarization ought to be. Conceive a beam of plane-polarized light to move among a number of particles, all small compared with any of the wave-lengths. The foreign matter, if optically denser than air, may be supposed to *load* the æther so as to increase its *inertia* without altering its

* *Phil. Mag.* S. 4, vol. xxxvii, p. 388.

resistance to distortion, provided that we agree to neglect effects analogous to chromatic dispersion. If the particles were away, the wave would pass on unbroken and no light would be emitted laterally. Even with the particles retarding the motion of the æther, the same will be true if, to counterbalance the increased inertia, suitable forces are caused to act on the æther at all points where the inertia is altered. These forces have the same period and *direction* as the undisturbed luminous vibrations themselves. The light actually emitted laterally is thus the same as would be caused by forces exactly the opposite of these acting on the medium otherwise free from disturbance; and it only remains to see what the effect of such forces would be.

On account of the smallness of the particles, the forces acting throughout the volume of any one are all of the same intensity and direction, and may be considered as a whole. The determination of the motion in the æther, due to the action of a periodic force at a given point, requires, of course, the aid of mathematical analysis; but very simple considerations will lead us to a conclusion on the particular point now under discussion. In the first place there is a complete symmetry round the direction of the force. The disturbance, consisting of transverse vibrations, is propagated outwards in all directions from the centre; and in consequence of the symmetry, the direction of vibration in any ray lies in the plane containing the ray and the axis; that is to say, the direction of vibration in the scattered or diffracted ray makes with the direction of vibration in the incident or primary ray the least possible angle. The symmetry also requires that the intensity of the scattered light should vanish for the ray which would be propagated along the axis; for there is nothing to distinguish one direction transverse to the ray from another. We have now got what we want. Suppose, for distinctness of statement, that the primary ray is vertical, and that the plane of vibration is that of the meridian. The intensity of the light scattered by a small particle is constant, and a maximum, for rays which lie in the vertical plane running east and west, *while there is no scattered ray along the north and south line*. If the primary ray is unpolarized, the light scattered north and south is entirely due to that component which vibrates east and west, and is therefore *perfectly polarized*, the direction of its vibration being also east and west. Similarly any other ray scattered horizontally is perfectly polarized, and the vibration is performed in the horizontal plane. In other directions the polarization becomes less and less complete as we approach the vertical, and in the vertical direction itself altogether disappears.

So far, then, as disturbance by very small particles is concerned, theory appears to be in complete accordance with the experiments of Tyndall and others. At the same time, if the above reasoning be valid, the question as to the direction of the vibrations in polarized light is decided in accordance with the view of Fresnel. Indeed the observation on the plane of polarization of the scattered light is virtually only another form of Professor Stokes's original test with the diffraction-grating. In its present shape, however, it is free from certain difficulties both of theory and experiment, which have led different physicists who have used the other method to contradictory conclusions. I confess I cannot see any room for doubt as to the result it leads to*.

The argument used is apparently open to a serious objection, which I ought to notice. It seems to prove too much. For if one disturbing particle is unable to send out a scattered ray in the direction of original vibration, it would appear that no combination of them (such as a small body may be supposed to be) could do so, at least at such a distance that the body subtends only a small solid angle. Now we know that when light vibrating in the plane of incidence falls on a reflecting surface at an angle of 45°,

* I only mean that *if* light, as is generally supposed, consists of transversal vibrations similar to those which take place in an elastic solid, the vibration must be normal to the plane of polarization. There is unquestionably a formal analogy between the two sets of phenomena extending over a very wide range; but it is another thing to assert that the vibrations of light are really and truly to-and-fro motions of a medium having mechanical properties (with reference to small vibrations) like those of ordinary solids. The fact that the theory of elastic solids led Green to Fresnel's formulae for the reflection and refraction of polarized light seems amply sufficient to warrant its employment here, while the question whether the analogy is more than formal is still left open.

light *is* sent out according to the law of ordinary reflection, whose direction of vibration is perpendicular to that in the incident ray. And not only is this so in experiment, but it has been proved by Green* to be a consequence of the very same view as to the nature of the difference between media of various refrangibilities as has been adopted in this paper. The apparent contradiction, however, is easily explained. It is true that the disturbance due to a foreign body of any size is the same as would be caused by forces acting through the space it fills in a direction parallel to that in which the primary light vibrates; *but these forces must be supposed to act on the medium as it actually is—that is, with the variable density*. Only on the supposition of complete uniformity would it follow that no ray could be emitted parallel to the line in which the forces act. When, however, the sphere of disturbance is small compared with the wave-length, the want of uniformity is of little account, and cannot alter the law regulating the intensity of the vibration propagated in different directions.

Having disposed of the polarization, let us now consider how the intensity of the scattered light varies from one part of the spectrum to another, still supposing that all the particles are many times smaller than the wave-length even of violet light. The whole question admits of analytical treatment; but before entering upon that, it may be worth while to show how the principal result may be anticipated from a consideration of the *dimensions* of the quantities concerned.

The object is to compare the intensities of the incident and scattered rays; for these will clearly be proportional. The number (i) expressing the ratio of the two amplitudes is a function of the following quantities:—T, the volume of the disturbing particle; r, the distance of the point under consideration from it; λ, the wave-length; b, the velocity of propagation of light; D and D', the original and altered densities: of which the first three depend only on space, the fourth on space and time, while the fifth and sixth introduce the consideration of mass. Other elements of the problem there are none, except mere numbers and angles, which

* *Camb. Phil. Trans.* vol. VII, 1837.

D

do not depend on the fundamental measurements of space, time, and mass. Since the ratio i, whose expression we seek, is of no dimensions in mass, it follows at once that D and D' only occur under the form $D : D'$, which is a simple number and may therefore be omitted. It remains to find how i varies with T, r, λ, b.

Now, of these quantities, b is the only one depending on time; and therefore, as i is of no dimensions in time, b cannot occur in its expression. We are left, then, with T, r, and λ; and from what we know of the dynamics of the question, we may be sure that i varies directly as T and inversely as r, and must therefore be proportional to $T \div \lambda^2 r$, T being of three dimensions in space. In passing from one part of the spectrum to another λ is the only quantity which varies, and we have the important law:—

When light is scattered by particles which are very small compared with any of the wave-lengths, the ratio of the amplitudes of the vibrations of the scattered and incident light varies inversely as the square of the wave-length, and the intensity of the lights themselves as the inverse fourth power.

I will now investigate the mathematical expression for the disturbance propagated in any direction from a small particle which a beam of light strikes.

Let the vibration corresponding to the incident light be expressed by $A \cos (2\pi bt/\lambda)$. The acceleration is

$$- A \left(\frac{2\pi}{\lambda} b\right)^2 \cos \frac{2\pi}{\lambda} bt;$$

so that the force which would have to be applied to the parts where the density is D', in order that the wave might pass on undisturbed, is, per unit of volume,

$$- (D' - D) A \left(\frac{2\pi b}{\lambda}\right)^2 \cos \frac{2\pi}{\lambda} bt.$$

To obtain the total force which must be supposed to act over the space occupied by the particle, the factor T must be introduced. The opposite of this conceived to act at O (the position of the particle) gives the same disturbance in the medium as is actually caused by the presence of the particle. Suppose, now, that the ray is incident along OY, and that the direction of vibration makes an angle α with the axis of x, which is the line of the scattered ray under consideration—a supposition which involves no loss of generality, because of the symmetry which we have shown to exist round the line of action of the force. The question is now entirely reduced to the discovery of the disturbance produced in the æther by a given periodic force acting at a fixed point in it. In his valuable paper "On the Dynamical Theory of Diffraction"*, Professor Stokes has given a complete investigation of this problem; and I might assume the result at once. The method there used is, however, for this particular purpose very indirect, and accordingly I have thought it advisable to give a comparatively short cut to the result, which will be found at the end of the present paper. It is proved that if the total force acting at O in the manner supposed be $F \cos (2\pi bt/\lambda)$, the resulting disturbance in the ray propagated along OX is

$$\zeta = \frac{F \sin \alpha}{4\pi b^2 Dr} \cos \frac{2\pi}{\lambda} (bt - r).$$

Substituting for F its value, we have

$$\zeta = A \frac{D' - D}{D} \frac{\pi T}{r\lambda^2} \sin \alpha \cos \frac{2\pi}{\lambda} (bt - r),$$

an equation which includes all our previous results and more.

One reservation, however, must not be omitted. Since we have supposed the medium uniform throughout, whereas it really has a different density at the place where the force acts, our investigation does not absolutely correspond to the actual circumstances of the case. As before remarked, no error is on that account to be feared in the law determining the intensity of the vibration in different directions; but it is probable that the coefficient, so far as it depends on $D : D'$, may be changed, and there may be a change in the phase comparable with $(2\pi/\lambda) \times$ the linear dimension of the particle, which is of importance when the scattered and primary waves have to be compounded.

* *Camb. Phil. Trans.* vol. IX, p. 1, 1849.

Editorial Conclusion

The author continues his analysis by considering the scattering effect of a very large number of particles, and derives agreement with his preliminary results. He compares his conclusions successfully with some actual observations. Rayleigh was rarely willing to settle for mathematical results without some comparisons with relevant experimental data obtained either by himself or others.

On the Manufacture and Theory of Diffraction-Gratings (1874)

[*Philosophical. Magazine.* XLVII, pp. 81–93, 193–205, 1874]

Editorial Preface

This paper consists essentially of two parts. The first is a reflection of Rayleigh's interest in the economical production of diffraction gratings. He discusses his experimentation with two methods, the first involving copying a given grating by photography and the second copying by contact printing. He cites reasons for believing that the first method will not be very effective and then goes on to discuss in detail his experimentation with the second. This part of the paper is too long for reproduction here.

The second part is devoted to theoretical investigations concerning gratings as light-analyzing instruments. The most important contribution was Rayleigh's derivation of the expression for the resolving power of a grating. Certain relevant extracts are presented here.

In a "Preliminary note on the Reproduction of Diffraction-Gratings by means of Photography," published in the *Proccedings of the Royal Society* for 1872, and in the *Philosophical Magazine* for November of the same year [Art. 17], I gave a short account of experiments with which I had been for some time occupied. A few further details were communicated to the British Association at Brighton (*Brit. Assoc. Report,* p. 39) [Art. 18]. I now propose to give the results of more recent experience in the practical manufacture of gratings, as well as some theoretical conclusions which have been in manuscript since the subject first engaged my attention.

There are two distinct methods of copying practised by the photographer—(1) by means of the camera, (2) by contact-printing. The first, if it were practicable for our purpose, would have the advantage of leaving the scale arbitrary, so that copies of varying degrees of fineness might be taken from the same original. By this method I have obtained a photograph of a piece of striped stuff on such a scale that there was room for about 200 lines in front of the pupil of the eye, capable of showing lateral images of a candle; but I soon found that the inherent imperfections of our optical appliances, if not the laws of light themselves, interposed an almost insuperable obstacle to obtaining adequate results.

However perfect a lens may be, there is a limit to its powers of condensing light into a point. Even if the source from which the light proceeds be infinitely small, the image still consists of a spot of finite size surrounded by dark and bright rings. That this must be so may be shown by general considerations without any calculations. If a lens is absolutely free from aberration, the secondary waves issuing from the different parts of its hinder surface agree perfectly in phase at the focal point. Let us consider the illumination at a neighbouring point in the focal plane. If the distance between the two points is so small that the difference of the distances between the point under consideration and the nearest and furthest parts of the object-glass is but a small fraction of the wave-length (λ), the group of secondary waves are still sensibly in agreement, and therefore give a resultant illumination the same as before. At a certain distance from the focal point the secondary waves divide themselves into two mutually destructive groups, corresponding to the nearer and further parts of the object-glass. There is therefore here a dark ring. Further out there is again light, then another dark ring, and so on, the intensity of the bright rings, however, rapidly diminishing.

The radius r of the first dark ring subtends at the centre of the lens an angle θ given by

$$\sin \theta = \cdot 61 \, \frac{\lambda}{R} *,$$

where R is the radius of the lens. If f be the focal length, we have

$$r = \cdot 61 \, \frac{f \lambda}{R}.$$

* Verdet, *Leçons d'Optique Physique*, vol. I p. 305.

Let us now suppose that the problem is to cover a square inch with 3000 lines. On account of the curvature of the field it would be impossible to obtain extreme definition over the surface of a square inch with a less focal distance than (say) four inches. If we take $f = 4$ and $\lambda = \frac{1}{40,000}$, we find

$$R = \frac{\cdot 61}{10,000 \, r},$$

which gives $R = \cdot 2$ for $r = \frac{1}{3000}$. That is to say, if the focal length were 4 inches and aperture $\cdot 4$ inch, the first dark ring corresponding to one of the lines would fall on the focal point of the neighbouring one—a state of things apparently inconsistent with good definition. It is true that the aperture might well be greater than half an inch, so that it may seem possible to satisfy the requirements of the case. But the result of the above calculation, being founded on the supposition of entire freedom from aberration, both spherical and chromatic, is subject in practice to a large modification. In astronomical telescopes, where everything is sacrificed to the requirement of extreme definition at the centre of the field, the theoretical limit is sometimes closely approached; but the case is very different with a photographic lens. In fact the very first thing it occurs to a photographer to do, when he wishes to improve the definition, is to contract the aperture of his lens by means of a stop—a course which would be attended with the opposite result in the case of a perfect object-glass, or even a good astronomical telescope. While, therefore, it might be too much to say that the reproduction of 3000 lines in an inch by lens and camera is impossible, the attempt to do so without very special appliances appears in a high degree unpromising. It would certainly require a lens more than usually free from spherical aberration, and unlike either a telescopic or a photographic object-glass, achromatic (if the expression may be allowed) for the chemical rays, unless indeed the latter requirement could be evaded by using approximately homogeneous light. It must be understood that nothing is here said against the practicability of covering a small space with lines *at the rate of* 3000 to the inch, a feat probably well within the powers of a good microscopic object-glass.

The method of contact-printing, on the other hand, is free from optical difficulties. The photographic film prepared on a flat piece of glass (or other support) may be brought by moderate pressure in a printing-frame within a very short distance of the lines of the original grating; and if the source of light be moderately small and the rays fall perpendicularly, the copy rarely fails in definition, unless through some photographic defect. When direct processes not depending on development are employed, the unclouded light of the sun is necessary. To avoid too much diffused light, I usually place the printing-frame on the floor of a room into which the sun shines, and adjust its position until the light reflected from the plate-glass front is sent back approximately in the direction of the sun. Too much time should not be lost in this operation, which requires no particular precision. Usually I cut off part of the extraneous light by partially closing the shutters; but I cannot say whether this makes any difference in the result. Those who are accustomed to this kind of experimenting will know that it is often less trouble to take a precaution than to find out whether it is really necessary. In an early stage of an investigation, when the causes of failure are numerous and unknown, it is best to exclude everything that can possibly be supposed to be prejudicial. When the principal difficulties have been overcome, it will be time enough to determine what precautions are necessary, if the question has not been already settled by accidental experience.

The remainder of this paper is principally occupied with theoretical considerations relating to the performance of gratings considered as light-analyzing apparatus. The more popular works on the theory of light give only the main outlines of the subject, and pass over almost in silence the important questions of illumination and definition. On the other hand, the mathematical treatises, such as Airy's "Tracts" and Verdet's *Leçons* though they give analytical results involving most of the required information, are occupied rather with explaining the production of spectra as a diffraction-phenomenon than with investigating on what conditions their perfection depends. On examining the question for myself, I came to the conclusion that the theory of gratings, as usually presented, is encumbered with a good deal that may properly be regarded as extraneous.

One of the first things to be noticed is the extraordinary precision required in the ruling. The difference of wave-length of the two sodium-lines is about a thousandth part. If, therefore, we suppose that one grating has 1000 lines in the space where another has 1001, it is evident that the first grating would produce the same deviation for the less-refrangible D line that the second would produce for the more-refrangible D line. We have only to suppose the two combined into one in order to see that, in a grating required to resolve the D line, there must be no systematic irregularity to the extent of a thousandth part of the small interval. Single lines may, of course, be out of position to a much larger amount. It is easy to see, too, that the same accuracy is required, whatever be the order of the spectrum examined.

The precision of ruling actually attained in gratings is very great. In the 3000 Nobert it is certain that the average interval between the lines does not vary by a six-thousandth part in passing from one half of the grating to the other; for the D lines, when well defined, do not appear so broad as a sixth part of the space separating them.

In considering the influence of the number of lines (n) and the order of the spectrum (m), we will suppose that the ruling is accurate, and that plane waves are incident perpendicularly upon the face of the grating whose width is represented in the figure by AB. But inasmuch as a large part of the phenomenon covered by the usual mathematical investigation depends upon the *limitation* of the grating at A and B, we shall find it convenient to take first the simple case of an aperture represented by AB, and afterwards to consider the influence of the ruling.

In the perpendicular direction BC all the secondary waves emanating from AB are in complete agreement of phase, and
D*

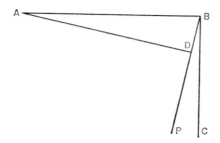

their resultant accordingly attains its highest possible value. In a direction *BP*, making with *BC* a very small angle, the agreement of phase will be disturbed. If *BP* be so drawn that the projection of *AB* upon it is equal to λ, the phases of the secondary waves will be distributed uniformly over a complete period, and the resultant will therefore be *nil*. The same result must ensue whenever *BD* is an exact multiple of λ.

We have now to consider the dependence of the *resolving-power* of a grating on the number of its lines (n) and the order of the spectrum observed (m).

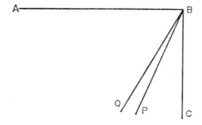

Let *BP* be the direction of the principal maximum for the wavelength λ in the mth spectrum; then the projection of *AB* on *BP* is $mn\lambda$ [representing the relative retardation of the extreme rays which pass through *A* and *B*]. If *BQ* be the direction corresponding to the first minimum, the projection of *AB* on *BQ* is $(mn + 1) \lambda$. Suppose now that $\lambda + \delta\lambda$ is the wavelength for which *BQ* gives the principal maximum, then

$$(mn + 1) \lambda = mn (\lambda + \delta\lambda);$$

whence

$$\frac{\delta\lambda}{\lambda} = \frac{1}{mn},$$

which shows that the resolving-power varies directly as *m* and *n**.

It is not possible to say precisely under what circumstances a double line would appear to be resolved—something no doubt would depend on the intensity of the light—but it seems probable that there would be no distinct resolution when the two images are separated by only half the width of the central band of either. If this be so, we may take $\lambda/m\delta\lambda$ as the least number of grooves capable of resolving in the *m*th spectrum a double line whose wave-lengths are λ and $\lambda + \delta\lambda$. In the case of the soda-lines $\delta\lambda/\lambda$ is about $\frac{1}{1000}$; and therefore to resolve them in the first spectrum would require 1000 grooves, in the second spectrum 500, and so on. It is evident that if the ruling be perfectly accurate and the illumination sufficient, the work may be accomplished with comparatively few lines by using a spectrum of elevated order.

The result of an attempt to determine experimentally the number of lines necessary to resolve *D* in the solar spectrum may here be recorded. The 3000-to-the-inch Nobert was used, its horizontal aperture being limited by the jaws of an adjustable slit. From the width of the slit found to be necessary the number of lines in operation was calculated.

In the first spectrum 1200 lines were required, in the second 630, and in the third 375. These numbers should be in the ratio 6:3:2; but the last, which presents the greatest deviation, was difficult of exact measurement.

Our Perception of the Direction of a Source of Sound (1876)

[*Nature*, XIV, pp. 32–33, 1876]

Editorial Preface

This is Rayleigh's first paper on the binaural effect and one of the first ever recorded. He was fascinated by this subject and returned to it later in life. These early experiments evidently convinced him that difference in intensity of sound at the two ears is insufficient to account for the ability to detect the direction of received sound. His later work indicated that *phase* difference is more decisive. This early work of Rayleigh stimulated an enormous amount of subsequent research in psychological acoustics.

The practical facility with which we recognize the situation of a sounding body has always been rather a theoretical difficulty. In the case of sight a special optical apparatus is provided whose function it is to modify the uniform excitation of the retina, which a luminous point, wherever situated, would otherwise produce. The mode of action of the crystalline lens of the eye is well understood, and the use of a lens is precisely the device that would at once occur to the mind of an optician ignorant of physiology. The bundle of rays, which would otherwise distribute themselves over the entire retina, and so give no indication of their origin, are made to converge upon a single point, whose excitation is to us the sign of an external object in a certain definite direction. If the luminous object is moved, the fact is at once recognized by the change in the point of excitation.

There is nothing in the ear corresponding to the crystalline lens of the eye, and this not accidentally, so to speak, but by the very nature of the case. The efficient action of a lens depends upon its diameter being at least many times greater than the wave-length of light, and for the purposes of sight there is no difficulty in satisfying this requirement. The wave-length of the rays by which we see is not much more than a ten-thousandth part of the diameter of the pupil of the eye. But when we pass to the case of sound and of the ear, the relative magnitudes of the corresponding quantities are altogether different. The waves of sound issuing from a man's mouth are about eight feet long, whereas the diameter of the passage of the ear is quite small, and could not well have been made a large multiple of eight feet. It is evident therefore that it is useless to look for anything corresponding to the crystalline lens of the eye, and that our power of telling the origin of a sound must be explained in some different way.

It has long been conjectured that the explanation turns upon the combined use of both ears; though but little seems to have been done hitherto in the way of bringing this view to the test. The observations and calculations now brought forward are very incomplete, but may perhaps help to clear the ground, and will have served their purpose if they induce others to pursue the subject.

The first experiments were made with the view of finding out with what degree of accuracy the direction of sound could be determined, and for this it was necessary of course that the observer should have no other material for his judgment than that contemplated.

The observer, stationed with his eyes closed in the middle of a lawn on a still evening, was asked to point with the hand in the direction of voices addressed to him by five or six assistants, who continually shifted their position. It was necessary to have several assistants, since it was found that otherwise their steps could be easily followed. The uniform result was that the direction of a human voice used in anything like a natural manner could be told with certainty from a single word, or even vowel, to within a few degrees.

But with other sounds the result was different. If the source was on the right or the left of the observer, its position could be told approximately, but it was uncertain whether, for example, a low whistle was in front or behind. This result led us to try a simple sound, such as that given by a fork mounted on a resonance-box. It was soon found that whatever might be the case with a truly simple sound, the observer never failed to detect the situation of the fork by the noises accompanying its excitation, whether this was done by striking or by a violin bow. It was therefore nceessary to arrange the experiment differently. Two assistants at equal distances and in opposite directions were provided with similar forks and resonators. At a signal given by a fourth, both forks were struck, but only one was held over its resonator, and the observer was asked to say, without moving his head, which he heard. When the observer was so turned that one fork was immediately in front and the other immediately behind, it was impossible for him to tell which fork was sounding, and if asked to say one or the other, felt that he was only guessing. But on turning a quarter round, so as to have one fork on his right and the other on his left, he could tell without fail, and with full confidence in being correct.

The possibility of distinguishing a voice in front from a voice behind would thus appear to depend on the compound character of the sound in a way that it is not easy to understand, and for which the second ear would be of no advantage. But even in the case of a lateral sound the matter is not free from difficulty, for the difference of intensity with which a lateral sound is perceived by the two ears is not great. The experiment may easily be tried roughly by stopping one ear with the hand, and turning round backwards and forwards while listening to a sound held steadily. Calculation shows, moreover, that the human head, considered as an obstacle to the waves of sound, is scarcely big enough in relation to the wave-length to give a sensible shadow. To throw light on this subject I have calculated the intensity of sound due to a distant source at the various points on the surface of a fixed spherical obstacle. The result depends on the ratio (α) between the circumference of the sphere and the length of the wave. If we call the point on the spherical surface nearest to the source the anterior pole, and the opposite point (where the shadow might be expected to be most intense) the posterior pole, the results on three suppositions as to the relative magnitudes of the sphere and wave-length are given in the following table:—

	$a = 2$	$a = 1$	$a = \frac{1}{2}$
Anterior Pole	·690	·503	·294
Posterior Pole	·318	·285	·260
Equator	·356	·237	·232

When, for example, the circumference of the sphere is but half the wavelength, the intensity at the posterior pole is only about a tenth part less than at the anterior pole, while the intensity is least of all in a lateral direction. When a is less than $\frac{1}{2}$, the difference of the intensities at the two poles is still less important, amounting to about one per cent., when $a = \frac{1}{4}$.

The value of a depends on the wave-length, which may vary within pretty wide limits, and it might be expected that the facility of distinguishing a lateral sound would diminish when the sound is grave. Experiments were accordingly tried with forks of a frequency of 128, but no greater difficulty was experienced than with forks of a frequency of 256, except such as might be attributed to the inferior loudness of the former. According to calculation the difference of intensity would here be too small to account for the power of discrimination.

On the Application of the
Principle of Reciprocity to Acoustics (1876)

[*Proceedings of the Royal Society*, xxv, pp. 118–122, 1876]

Editorial Preface

In this paper Rayleigh disposes of some difficulties which at first sight seemed to impugn the validity of the celebrated reciprocity theorem of Helmholtz in its acoustical application. Rayleigh was much interested in principles of this kind and devoted much attention to them later in his *Theory of Sound*. The article illustrates both the author's grasp of the essential physical content of the theorem and his insight into rather complicated experimental situations. The theorem, of course, has had wide application in modern acoustics in connection with the calibration of transducers.

In a memoir published some years ago by Helmholtz (*Crelle*, Bd. LVII.) it was proved that if a uniform frictionless gaseous medium be thrown into vibration by a simple source of sound of given period and intensity, the variation of pressure is the same at any point *B* when the source of sound is at *A* as it would have been at *A* had the source of sound been situated at *B*, and that this law is not interfered with by the presence of any number of fixed solid obstacles on which the sound may impinge.

A simple source of sound is a point at which the condition of continuity of the fluid is broken by an alternate introduction and abstraction of fluid, given in amount and periodic according to the harmonic law.

The reciprocal property is capable of generalization so as to apply to all acoustical systems whatever capable of vibrating about a configuration of equilibrium, as I proved in the *Proceedings of the Mathematical Society* for June 1873 [Art. 21], and is not lost even when the systems are subject to damping, provided that the frictional forces vary as the first power of the velocity, as must always be the case when the motion is small enough. Thus Helmholtz's theorem may be extended to the case when the medium is not uniform, and when the obstacles are of such a character that they share the vibration.

But although the principle of reciprocity appears to be firmly grounded on the theoretical side, instances are not uncommon in which a sound generated in the open air at a point A is heard at a distant point B, when an equal or even more powerful sound at B fails to make itself heard at A; and some phenomena of this kind are strongly insisted upon by Prof. Henry in opposition to Prof. Tyndall's views as to the importance of "acoustic clouds" in relation to the audibility of fog-signals. These observations were not, indeed, made with the simple sonorous sources of theory; but there is no reason to suppose that the result would have been different if simple sources could have been used.

In experiments having for their object the comparison of sounds heard under different circumstances there is one necessary precaution to which it may not be superfluous to allude, depending on the fact that the audibility of a particular sound depends not only upon the strength of that sound, but also upon the strength of other sounds which may be heard along with it. For example, a lady seated in a closed carriage and carrying on a conversation through an open window in a crowded thoroughfare will hear what is said to her far more easily than she can make herself heard in return; but this is no failure in the law of reciprocity.

The explanation of his observations given by Henry depends upon the peculiar action of wind, first explained by Prof. Stokes. According to this view a sound is ordinarily heard better with the wind than against it, in consequence of a curvature of the rays. With the wind a ray will generally be bent downwards, since the velocity of the air is generally greater overhead than at the surface, and therefore the upper part of the wave-front tends to gain on the lower. The ray which ultimately reaches the observer is one which started in some degree upwards from the source, and has the advantage of being out of the way of obstacles for the greater part of its course. Against the wind, on the other hand, the curvature of the rays is upwards, so that a would-be observer at a considerable distance is in danger of being left in a sound-shadow.

It is very important to remark that this effect depends, not upon the mere existence of a wind, but upon the velocity of the wind being greater overhead than below. A uniform translation of the entire atmosphere would be almost without effect. In particular cases it may happen that the velocity of the wind diminishes with height, and then sound is best transmitted *against* the wind. Prof. Henry shows that several anomalous phenomena relating to the audibility of signals may be explained by various suppositions as to the velocity of the wind at different heights. When the distances concerned are great, comparatively small curvatures of the ray may produce considerable results.

There is a further possible consequence of the action of wind (or variable temperature), which, so far as I know, has not hitherto been remarked. By making the velocity a suitable function of height it would be possible to secure an actual convergence of rays in a vertical plane upon a particular station. The atmosphere would then act like the lens of a lighthouse, and the intensity of sound might be altogether abnormal. This may perhaps be the explanation of the extraordinary distances at which guns have sometimes been heard.

The difference in the propagation of sound against and with the wind is no exception to the general law referred to at the beginning of this communication, for that law applies only to the vibrations of a system about a configuration of equilibrium. A motion of the medium is thus excluded. But the bending of the sound-ray due to a variable temperature, to which attention has been drawn by Prof. Reynolds, does not interfere with the application of the law.

An experiment has, however, been brought forward by Prof. Tyndall, in which there is an apparent failure of reciprocity not referable to any motion of the medium*. The source of sound is a very high-pitched reed mounted in a short tube and blown from

* *Proc. Roy. Inst.* January 1875; also Prof. Tyndall's work on *Sound*, 3rd edition.

a small bellows with which it is connected by rubber tubing. The variation of pressure at the second point is made apparent by means of the sensitive flame, which has been used by Prof. Tyndall with so much success on other occasions. Although the flame itself, when unexcited, is 18 to 24 inches high, it was proved by a subsidiary experiment that the root of the flame, where it issues from the burner, is the seat of sensitiveness. With this arrangement the effect of a cardboard or glass screen interposed between the reed and the flame was found to be different, according as the screen was close to the flame or close to the reed. In the former case the flame indicated the action of sound, but in the latter remained uninfluenced. Since the motion of the screen is plainly equivalent to an interchange of the reed and flame, there is to all appearance a failure in the law of reciprocity.

At first sight this experiment is difficult to reconcile with theoretical conclusions. It is true that the conditions under which reciprocity is to be expected are not very perfectly realized, since the flame ought not to be moved from one position to the other. Although the seat of sensitiveness may be limited to the root of the flame, the tall column of highly heated gas might not be without effect; and in fact it appeared to me possible that the response of the flame, when close to the screen, might be due to the conduction of sound downwards along it. Not feeling satisfied, however, with this explanation, I determined to repeat the experiment, and wrote to Prof. Tyndall, asking to be allowed to see the apparatus. In reply he very kindly proposed to arrange a repetition of the experiment at the Royal Institution for my benefit, an offer which I gladly accepted.

The effect itself was perfectly distinct, and, as it soon appeared, was not to be explained in the manner just suggested, since the response of the flame when close to the screen continued, even when the upper part of the heated column was protected from the direct action of the source by additional screens interposed. I was more than ever puzzled until Mr Cottrell showed me another experiment in which, I believe, the key of the difficulty is to be found.

When the axis of the tube containing the reed is directed towards the flame, situated at a moderate distance, there is a distinct and immediate response; but when the axis is turned away from the flame through a comparatively small angle, the effect ceases, although the distance is the same as before, and there are no obstacles interposed. If now a cardboard screen is held in the prolongation of the axis of the reed, and at such an angle as to reflect the vibrations in the direction of the flame, the effect is again produced with the same apparent force as at first.

These results prove conclusively that the reed does not behave as the simple source of theory, even approximately. When the screen is close (about 2 inches distant) the more powerful vibrations issuing along the axis of the instrument impinge directly upon the screen, are reflected back, and take no further part in the experiment. The only vibrations which have a chance of reaching the flame, after diffraction round the screen, are the comparatively feeble ones which issue nearly at right angles with the axis. On the other hand, when the screen is close to the flame, the efficient vibrations are those which issue at a small angle with the axis, and are therefore much more powerful. Under these circumstances it is not surprising that the flame is affected in the latter case and not in the former.

The concentration of sound in the direction of the axis is greater than would have been anticipated, and is to be explained by the very short wave-length corresponding to the pitch of the reed. If, as is not improbable, the overtones of the note given by the reed are the most efficient part of the sound, the wave-length will be still shorter and the concentration more easy to understand*.

The reciprocal theorem in its generalized form is not restricted to simple sources, from which (in the absence of obstacles) sound would issue alike in all directions; and the statement for *double sources* will throw light on the subject of this note. A double source may be thus defined:—Conceive two equal and opposite

---

* July 13. I have lately observed that the flame in question is extremely sensitive to one of Mr F. Galton's whistles, which gives notes near the limits of ordinary hearing.

simple sources, situated at a short distance apart, to be acting simultaneously. By calling the two sources opposite, it is meant that they are to be at any moment in opposite phases. At a moderate distance the effects of the two sources are antagonistic and may be made to neutralize one another to any extent by diminishing the distance between the sources. If, however, at the same time that we diminish the interval, we augment the intensity of the single sources, the effect may be kept constant. Pushing this idea to its limit, when the intensity becomes infinite and the interval vanishes, we arrive at the conception of a double source having an axis of symmetry coincident with the line joining the single sources of which it is composed. In an open space the effect of a double source is the same as that communicated to the air by the vibration of a solid sphere whose centre is situated at the double point and whose line of vibration coincides with the axis, and the intensity of sound in directions inclined to the axis varies as the square of the cosine of the obliquity.

The statement of the reciprocal theorem with respect to double sources is then as follows:—If there be equal double sources at two points A and B, having axes AP, BQ respectively, then the *velocity* of the medium at B resolved in the direction BQ due to the source at A is the same as the *velocity* at A resolved in the direction AP due to the source at B. If the waves observed at A and B are sensibly plane, and if the axes AP, BQ are equally inclined to the waves received, we may, in the above statement, replace "velocities" by "pressures," but not otherwise.

Suppose, now, that equal double sources face each other, so that the common axis is AB, and let us examine the effect of interposing a screen near to A. By the reciprocal theorem, whether there be a screen or not, the velocity at A in direction AB due to B is equal to the velocity at B in direction AB due to A. The waves received at B are approximately plane and perpendicular to AB, so that the relation between the velocity and pressure at B is that proper to a plane wave; but it is otherwise in the case of the sound received at A. Accordingly the reciprocal theorem does not lead us to expect an equality between the pressures at A and

B, on which quantities the behaviour of the sensitive flames depends*. On the contrary, it would appear that the pressure at *A* corresponding to the given velocity along *AB* should be much greater than in the case of a plane wave, and then the relative advantage of the position *A* would be explained.

It will be seen that if the preceding arguments are correct, Prof. Tyndall's experiment does not bear out the conclusions that he has based upon it with respect to the observations of the French Commission at Villejuif and Montlhéry. No acoustic clouds could explain the failure of reciprocity then observed; and the more probable hypothesis that the effect was due to wind is not inconsistent with the observation that the air (at the surface) was moving in the direction against which the sound was best heard.

Further experiments on this subject are very desirable.

* [1899. See however *Phil. Mag.* vol. vii, p. 153, 1879, where it appears that the excitation of a flame is due, not to a variable *pressure*, but to transverse *motion* across the nozzle.]

On the Stability, or Instability, of Certain Fluid Motions (1880)

[*Proceedings of the London Mathematical Society*, XI, pp. 57–70, 1880]

Editorial Introduction

This is the second paper Rayleigh wrote on the stability of fluid flow, a subject he recurred to many times in his professional career. There is no doubt that his interest here was stimulated first by his concern for the acoustical properties of sensitive flames. In this paper he removes certain difficulties inherent in his first article. Ludwig Prandtl (*Essentials of Fluid Dynamics*, English translation, Blackie & Son Ltd., 1952, p. 113) comments that in this and two subsequent papers in 1887 and 1895, Rayleigh made the first investigations of the important problem of the result of small disturbances imposed on a given fluid motion. This work therefore initiated the studies of turbulence in fluid flow which have proved of great importance particularly in modern aerodynamics. When Rayleigh wrote this first paper Osborne Reynolds had not yet applied dimensional analysis and the theory of dynamical similitude to problems of fluid flow. Rayleigh commented on Reynolds' result in a later paper ("On the Question of the Stability of the Flow of Fluids", *Phil. Mag.* **34**, 59 (1892); Art. 194 in Rayleigh's *Scientific Papers*), but evidently felt that a complete dynamical analysis was preferable to results obtained by the method of dimensions in this case.

In a former communication to the Society "On the Instability of Jets"*, I applied a method due to Sir W. Thomson, to calculate the manner of falling away from equilibrium of jets bounded by one or more surfaces of discontinuity. Such interest as these investigations possessed was due principally to the possibility of applying their results to the explanation of certain acoustical phenomena relating to sensitive flames and smoke jets. But it soon appeared that in one important respect the calculations failed to correspond with the facts.

To fix the ideas, let us take the case of an originally plane surface

* *London Math. Soc. Proc.*, vol. X, p. 4 Nov. 14, 1878. [Art. 58.]

111

of separation, on the two sides of which the fluid moves with
equal and opposite constant velocities ($\pm V$). In equilibrium the
elevation h, at every point x along the surface, is zero. It is
proved that, if initially the surface be at rest in the form defined
by $h = H \cos kx$, then, after a time t, its form is given by

$$h = H \cos kx \cdot \cosh kVt, \qquad (1)$$

provided that, throughout the whole time contemplated, the
disturbance is small. In the same sense as that in which the
frequency of vibration measures the stability of a system vibrating about a configuration of stable equilibrium, so the coefficient
kV of t, in equations such as (1), measures the instability of
an unstable system; and we see, in the present case, that the
instability increases without limit with k; that is to say, the
shorter the wave-length of the sinuosities on the surface of
separation, the more rapidly are they magnified.

The application of this result to sensitive jets would lead us to
the conclusion that their sensitiveness increases indefinitely with
pitch. It is true that, in the case of certain flames, the pitch of the
most efficient sounds is very high, not far from the upper limit of
human hearing; but there are other kinds of sensitive jets on
which these high sounds are without effect, and which require for
their excitation a moderate or even a grave pitch.

A probable explanation of the discrepancy readily suggests
itself. The calculations are founded upon the supposition that the
changes of velocity are discontinuous—a supposition which
cannot possibly agree with reality. In consequence of fluid friction
a surface of discontinuity, even if it could ever be formed, would
instantaneously disappear, the transition from the one velocity to
the other becoming more and more gradual, until the layer of
transition attained a sensible width. When this width is comparable with the wave-length of the sinuosity, the solution for an
abrupt transition ceases to be applicable, and we have no reason
for supposing that the instability would increase for much shorter
wave-lengths.

In the following investigations, I shall suppose that the motion is entirely in two dimensions, parallel (say) to the plane xy, so that (in the usual notation) w is zero, as well as the rotations ξ, η. The rotation ζ parallel to z is connected with the velocities u, v by the equation

$$\zeta = \tfrac{1}{2}\left(\frac{du}{dy} - \frac{dv}{dx}\right). \tag{2}$$

When the phenomena under consideration are such that the compressibility may be neglected, the condition that no fluid is anywhere introduced or abstracted, gives

$$\frac{du}{dx} + \frac{dv}{dy} = 0. \tag{3}$$

In the absence of friction, ζ remains constant for every particle of the fluid; otherwise, if ν be the kinematic viscosity, the general equation for ζ is

$$\frac{\partial \zeta}{\partial t} = \xi \frac{dw}{dx} + \eta \frac{dw}{dy} + \zeta \frac{dw}{dz} + \nu\nabla\zeta*, \tag{4}$$

where

$$\partial/\partial t = d/dt + u d/dx + v d/dy + w d/dz, \tag{5}$$

and

$$\nabla = d^2/dx^2 + d^2/dy^2 + d^2/dz^2. \tag{6}$$

For the proposed applications to motion in two dimensions, these equations reduce to

$$\partial\zeta/\partial t = \nu\nabla\zeta, \tag{7}$$

$$\partial/\partial t = d/dt + u d/dx + v d/dy, \tag{8}$$

$$\nabla = d^2/dx^2 + d^2/dy^2, \tag{9}$$

while the two other equations similar to (4) are satisfied identically.

In order to investigate the influence of friction on stratified motion, we may now suppose that v is zero, while u and ζ are functions of y only. Our equations then give simply

$$d\zeta/dt = \nu\, d^2\zeta/dy^2, \tag{10}$$

* Lamb's *Motion of Fluids*, p. 243.

which shows that the rotation ζ is *conducted* according to precisely the same laws as heat. In the case of air at atmospheric pressure, the value of ν is, according to Maxwell's experiments, $\nu = \cdot16$*, not differing greatly from the number ($\cdot22$) corresponding to the conduction of temperature in *iron*.

The various solutions of (10), discovered by Fourier, are at once applicable to our present purpose. In the problem already referred to, of a surface of discontinuity $y = 0$, separating portions of fluid moving with different but originally constant velocities, the rotation is at first zero, except upon the surface itself, but it is rapidly diffused into the adjacent fluid. At time t its value at any point y is

$$\zeta = \int_{-\infty}^{+\infty} \zeta \, dy \cdot \frac{e^{-y^2/4\nu t}}{2\sqrt{(\pi \nu t)}}, \tag{11}$$

and

$$\int_{-\infty}^{+\infty} \zeta \, dy = \tfrac{1}{2} \int \frac{du}{dy} \, dy = \tfrac{1}{2}(V_2 - V_1), \tag{12}$$

if V_2, V_1 are the velocities on the postiive and negative sides of the surface respectively. If $y^2 = 4\nu t$, the value of ζ is less than that to be found at $y - 0$, in the ratio $e:1$. Thus, after a time t, the thickness of the layer of transition ($2y$) is comparable in magnitude with $1\cdot6 \sqrt{t}$; for example, after one second it may be considered to be about $1\tfrac{1}{2}$ centimetres. In the case of water, the coefficient of conductivity is much less. It seems that $\nu = \cdot014$; so that, after one second, the layer is about half a centimetre thick.

The circumstances of a two-dimensional jet will be represented by supposing the velocity to be limited initially to an infinitely thin layer at $y = 0$. It is convenient here to use the velocity u itself instead of ζ. Since $\zeta = \tfrac{1}{2} du/dy$,

$$du/dt = \nu \, d^2u/dy^2, \tag{13}$$

and thus the solution is of the same form as before:

$$u = \int_{-\infty}^{+\infty} u \, dy \cdot \frac{e^{-y^2/4\nu t}}{2\sqrt{(\pi \nu t)}}. \tag{14}$$

* The centimetre and second being units.

We may conclude that, however thin a jet of air may be initially, its thickness after one second is comparable with $1\frac{1}{2}$ centimetres. A similar calculation may be made for the case of a linear jet, whose whole velocity is originally concentrated in one line.

There is, therefore, ample foundation for the opinion that the phenomena of sensitive jets may be greatly influenced by fluid friction, and deviate materially from the results of calculations based upon the supposition of discontinuous changes of velocity. Under these circumstances, it becomes important to investigate the character of the equilibrium of stratified motion in cases more nearly approaching what is met with in practice. Fully to include the effects of friction, would immensely increase the difficulties of the problem. For the present, at least, we must treat the fluid as frictionless, and be satisfied if we can obtain solutions for laws of stratification which are free from discontinuity. For the undisturbed motion, the component velocity v is zero, and u is a function of y only. A curve, in which u is ordinate and y is abscissa, represents the law of stratification and may be called, for brevity, the velocity curve.

Editorial Comment

From this point the author proceeds to examine other types of velocity profiles. He also investigates cases in which the moving layers of fluid are bounded by fixed walls.

Address to the Mathematical and Physical Science Section of the British Association (1882)

[*British Association Report*, pp. 437–441, 1882]

Editorial Preface

Rayleigh was chairman of Section A of the British Association for the Advancement of Science in 1882. His address before the Section at the Southampton meeting of that year is here reproduced in full. Rayleigh wisely refrained from endeavoring to summarize recent progress in physics and mathematics in favor of making some general observations on the relation between mathematical theorizing in physics and experimental work: this led him further to discuss the problem of precision of measurement, where it is essential and where it is irrelevant. His illustrations, taken from sound, light and electrical measurements, reflect his own concern for problems on which he had recently been engaged.

In common with some of my predecessors in this chair, I recognise that probably the most useful form which a presidential address could take, would be a summary of the progress of physics, or of some important branch of physics, during recent years. But the difficulties of such a task are considerable, and I do not feel myself equal to grappling with them. The few remarks which I have to offer are of a general, I fear it may be thought of a commonplace character. All I can hope is that they may have the effect of leading us into a frame of mind suitable for the work that lies before us.

The diversity of the subjects which come under our notice in this section, as well as of the methods by which alone they can be adequately dealt with, although a sign of the importance of our work, is a source of considerable difficulty in the conduct of it. From the almost inevitable specialisation of modern science, it has come about that much that is familiar to one member of our section is unintelligible to another, and that details whose importance is obvious to the one fail altogether to rouse any interest in the mind of the other. I must appeal to the authors of papers to bear this difficulty in mind, and to confine within moderate limits their discussion of points of less general interest.

Even within the limits of those departments whose foundation is evidently experimental, there is room, and indeed necessity, for great variety of treatment. One class of investigators relies mainly upon reiterated appeals to experiment to resolve the questions which appear still to be open, while another prefers, with Thomas Young, to base its decisions as far as possible upon deductions from experiments already made by others. It is scarcely necessary to say that in the present state of science both methods are indispensable. Even where we may fairly suppose that the fundamental principles are well established, careful and often troublesome work is necessary to determine with accuracy the constants which enter into the expression of natural laws. In many cases the accuracy desirable, even from a practical point of view, is hard to attain. In many others, where the interest is mainly theoretical, we cannot afford to neglect the confirmations which our views may derive from the comparison of measurements made in different fields and in face of different experimental difficulties. Examples of the inter-dependence of measurements apparently distinct will occur to every physicist. I may mention the absolute determinations of electrical resistance, and of the amounts of heat developed from electrical and mechanical work, any two of which involve also the third, and the relation of the velocity of sound to the mechanical and thermal properties of air.

Where a measurement is isolated, and not likely to lead to the solution of any open question, it is doubtless possible to spend upon it time and attention that might with advantage be otherwise bestowed. In such a case we may properly be satisfied for a time with work of a less severe and accurate character, knowing that with the progress of knowledge the way is sure to be smoothed both by a better appreciation of the difficulties involved and by the invention of improved experimental appliances. I hope I shall not be misunderstood as underrating the importance of great accuracy in its proper place if I express the opinion that the desire for it has sometimes had a prejudicial effect. In cases where a rough result would have sufficed for all immediate purposes, no measurement at all has been attempted, because the circumstances rendered it unlikely that a high standard of precision could be attained. Whether our aim be more or less ambitious, it is important to recognise the limitations to which our methods are necessarily subject, and as far as possible to estimate the extent to which our results are uncertain. The comparison of estimates of uncertainty made before and after the execution of a set of measurements may sometimes be humiliating, but it is always instructive.

Even when our results show no greater discrepancies than we were originally prepared for, it is well to err on the side of modesty in estimating their trustworthiness. The history of science teaches only too plainly the lesson that no single method is absolutely to be relied upon, that sources of error lurk where they are least expected, and that they may escape the notice of the most experienced and conscientious worker. It is only by the concurrence of evidence of various kinds and from various sources that practical certainty may at last be attained, and complete confidence justified. Perhaps I may be allowed to illustrate my meaning by reference to a subject which has engaged a good deal of my attention for the last two years—the absolute measurement of electrical resistance. The unit commonly employed in this country is founded upon experiments made about twenty years ago by a distinguished committee of this Association, and was intended to represent an absolute resistance of 10^9. C.G.S., *i.e.* one ohm. The method employed by the committee at the recommendation of Sir W. Thomson (it had been originally proposed by Weber) consists in observing the deflection from the magnetic meridian of a needle suspended at the centre of a coil of insulated wire. This forms a closed circuit and is made to revolve with uniform and known speed about a vertical axis. From the speed and deflection, in combination with the mean radius of the coil and the number of its turns, the absolute resistance of the coil, and thence of any other standard, can be determined.

About ten years later Kohlrausch attacked the problem by another method, which it would take too long to explain, and arrived at the result that the B.A. unit was equal to 1·02 ohms—about two per cent too large. Rowland, in America, by a comparison between the steady battery current flowing in a primary coil with the transient current developed in a secondary coil when the primary current is reversed, found that the B.A. unit was ·991 ohms. Lorenz, using a different method again, found ·980, while H. Weber, from distinct experiments, arrived at the conclusion that the B.A. unit was correct. It will be seen that the results obtained by these highly competent observers range over about four per cent. Two new determinations have lately been made in the Cavendish laboratory at Cambridge, one by myself with the method of the revolving coil, and another by Mr Glazebrook, who used a modification of the method followed by Rowland, with the result that the B.A. unit is ·986 ohms. I am now engaged upon a third determination, using a method which is a modification of that of Lorenz.

In another important part of the field of experimental science, where the subject-matter is ill understood, and the work is qualitative rather than quantitative, success depends more directly upon sagacity and genius. It must be admitted that much labour spent in this kind of work is ill-directed. Bulky records of crude and uninterpreted observations are not science, nor even in many cases the raw material out of which science will be constructed. The door of experiment stands always open; and when the question is ripe, and the man is found, he will nine times out of ten find it necessary to go through the work again. Observations made by the way, and under unfavourable conditions, may often give rise to valuable suggestions, but these must be tested by experiment, in which the conditions are simplified to the utmost, before they can lay claim to acceptance.

When an unexpected effect is observed, the question will arise whether or not an explanation can be found upon admitted principles. Sometimes the answer can be quickly given; but more often it will happen that an assertion of what *ought* to have been expected can only be made as the result of an elaborate discussion of the circumstances of the case, and this discussion must generally be mathematical in its spirit, if not in its form. In repeating, at the beginning of the century, the well-known experiment of the inaudibility of a bell rung *in vacuo*, Leslie made the interesting observation that the presence of hydrogen was inimical to the production of sound, so that not merely was the sound less in hydrogen than in air of equal pressure, but that the actual addition of hydrogen to rarefied air caused a diminution in the intensity of sound. How is this remarkable fact to be explained? Does it prove, as Herschel was inclined to think, that a mixture of gases of widely different densities differs in its acoustical properties from a single gas? These questions could scarcely be answered satisfactorily but by a mathematical investigation of the process by which vibrations are communicated from a vibrating solid body to the surrounding gas. Such an investigation, founded exclusively upon principles well established before the date of Leslie's observation, was undertaken years afterwards by Stokes, who proved that what Leslie observed was exactly what ought to have been expected. The addition of hydrogen to attenuated air increases the wave-length of vibrations of given pitch, and consequently the facility with which the gas can pass round the edge of the bell from the advancing to the retreating face, and thus escape those rarefactions and condensations which are essential to the formation of a complete sound wave. There remains no reason for supposing that the phenomenon depends upon any other elements than the density and pressure of the gaseous atmosphere, and a direct trial, *e.g.* a comparison between air and a mixture of carbonic anhydride and hydrogen of like density, is almost superfluous.

Examples such as this, which might be multiplied *ad libitum*, show how difficult it often is for an experimenter rightly to interpret his results without the aid of mathematics. It is eminently desirable that the experimenter himself should be in a position to make the calculations, to which his work gives occasion, and from which in return he would often receive valuable hints for further experiment. I should like to see a course of mathematical instruction arranged with especial reference to physics, within which those whose bent was plainly towards experiment might, more or less completely, confine themselves. Probably a year spent judiciously on such a course would do more to qualify the student for actual work than two or three years of the usual mathematical curriculum. On the other side, it must be remembered that the human mind is limited, and that few can carry the weight of a complete mathematical armament without some repression of their energies in other directions. With many of us difficulty of remembering, if not want of time for acquiring, would impose an early limit. Here, as elsewhere, the natural advantages of a division of labour will assert themselves. Innate dexterity and facility in contrivance, backed by unflinching perseverance, may often conduct to successful discovery or invention a man who has little taste for speculation; and on the other hand the mathematician, endowed with genius and insight, may find a sufficient field for his energies in interpreting and systematising the work of others.

The different habits of mind of the two schools of physicists sometimes lead them to the adoption of antagonistic views on doubtful and difficult questions. The tendency of the purely experimental school is to rely almost exclusively upon direct evidence, even when it is obviously imperfect, and to disregard arguments which they stigmatise as theoretical. The tendency of the mathematician is to overrate the solidity of his theoretical structures, and to forget the narrowness of the experimental foundation upon which many of them rest.

By direct observation, one of the most experienced and successful experimenters of the last generation convinced himself that light of definite refrangibility was capable of further analysis by absorption. It has happened to myself, in the course of measurements of the absorbing power of various media for the different rays of the spectrum, to come across appearances at first sight

E

strongly confirmatory of Brewster's views, and I can therefore understand the persistency with which he retained his opinion. But the possibility of further analysis of light of definite refrangibility (except by polarisation) is almost irreconcilable with the wave theory, which on the strongest grounds had been already accepted by most of Brewster's contemporaries; and in consequence his results, though urgently pressed, failed to convince the scientific world. Further experiment has fully justified this scepticism, and in the hands of Airy, Helmholtz, and others, has shown that the phenomena by which Brewster was misled can be explained by the unrecognised intrusion of diffused light. The anomalies disappear when sufficient precaution is taken that the refrangibility of the light observed shall really be definite.

On similar grounds undulationists early arrived at the conviction that physically light and invisible radiant heat are both vibrations of the same kind, differing merely in wave-length; but this view appears to have been accepted slowly, and almost reluctantly, by the experimental school*.

When the facts which appear to conflict with theory are well defined and lend themselves easily to experiment and repetition, there ought to be no great delay in arriving at a judgment. Either the theory is upset, or the observations, if not altogether faulty, are found susceptible of another interpretation. The difficulty is greatest when the necessary conditions are uncertain, and their fulfilment rare and uncontrollable. In many such cases an attitude of reserve, in expectation of further evidence, is the only wise one. Premature judgments err perhaps as much on one side as on the other. Certainly in the past many extraordinary observations have met with an excessive incredulity. I may instance the fireballs which sometimes occur during violent thunderstorms. When the telephone was first invented, the early reports of its performances were discredited by many on quite insufficient grounds.

* [1900. The reader may refer to a paper on "The History of the Doctrine of Radiant Energy," *Phil. Mag.* xxvii, p. 265, 1889.] — [Art. 154.]

It would be an interesting, but too difficult and delicate a task, to enumerate and examine the various important questions which remain still undecided from the opposition of direct and indirect evidence. Merely as illustrations I will mention one or two in which I happen to have been interested. It has been sought to remedy the inconvenience caused by excessive reverberation of sound in cathedrals and other large unfurnished buildings by stretching wires overhead from one wall to another. In some cases no difference has been perceived, but in others it is thought that advantage has been gained. From a theoretical point of view it is difficult to believe that the wires could be of service. It is known that the vibrations of a wire do not communicate themselves in any appreciable degree directly to the air, but require the intervention of a sounding-board, from which we may infer that vibrations in the air would not readily communicate themselves to stretched wires. It seems more likely that the advantage supposed to have been gained in a few cases is imaginary than that the wires should really have played the part attributed to them.

The other subject on which, though with diffidence, I should like to make a remark or two, is that of Prout's law, according to which the atomic weights of the elements, or at any rate of many of them, stand in simple relation to that of hydrogen. Some chemists have reprobated strongly the importation of *à priori* views into the consideration of the question, and maintain that the only numbers worthy of recognition are the immediate results of experiment. Others, more impressed by the argument that the close approximations to simple numbers cannot be merely fortuitous, and more alive to the inevitable imperfections of our measurements, consider that the experimental evidence against the simple numbers is of a very slender character, balanced, if not outweighed, by the *à priori* argument in favour of simplicity. The subject is eminently one for further experiment; and as it is now engaging the attention of chemists, we may look forward to the settlement of the question by the present generation. The time has perhaps come when a redetermination of the densities of the principal gases may be desirable—an undertaking for which I have made some preparations*.

If there is any truth in the views that I have been endeavouring to impress, our meetings in this section are amply justified. If the progress of science demands the comparison of evidence drawn from different sources, and fully appreciated only by minds of different order, what may we not gain from the opportunities here given for public discussion, and, perhaps more valuable still, private interchange of opinion? Let us endeavour, one and all, to turn them to the best account.

* [1899. See *Proc. Roy. Soc.* XLIII, p. 356, 1888; L, p. 449, 1892; LIII, p. 134, 1893.] — [Art. 146; Art. 187; Art. 201.]

On an Instrument Capable of Measuring the Intensity of Aerial Vibrations (1882)

[*Philosophical Magazine*, xiv, pp. 186, 187, 1882]

Editorial Preface

This paper provides the first detailed description of what has since become known as the Rayleigh disk. This instrument in various modifications is still in use today in the absolute measurement of sound intensity.

This instrument arose out of an experiment described in the *Proceedings of the Cambridge Philosophical Society**, Nov. 1880, from which it appeared that a light disk, capable of rotation about a vertical diameter, tends with some decision to set itself at right angles to the direction of alternating aerial currents. In Fig. 1, *A* is a brass tube closed at one end with a glass plate *B*,

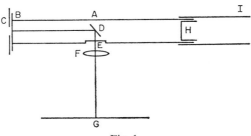

Fig. 1.

behind which is a slit *C* backed by a lamp. *D* is a light mirror with attached magnets, such as are used for reflecting-galvano-meters, and is suspended by a silk fibre. The light from the slit is

* See also *Proc. Roy. Soc.*, May 5, 1881, p. 110. [Art. 79.]

incident upon the mirror at an angle of 45°, and, after reflection, escapes from the tube through a glass window at E. It then falls upon a lens F, and throws an image of the slit upon a scale G. At a distance DH, equal to DC, the tube is closed by a diaphragm of tissue paper, beyond which it is acoustically prolonged by a sliding tube I.

When the instrument is exposed to sounds whose half wavelength is equal to CH, H becomes a node of the stationary vibrations, and the paper diaphragm offers but little impediment. Its office is to screen the suspended parts from accidental currents of air. At D there is a loop; and the mirror tends to set itself at right angles to the tube under the influence of the vibratory motion. This tendency is opposed by the magnetic forces; but the image upon the scale shifts its position through a distance proportional to the intensity of the action.

As in galvanometers, increased sensitiveness may be obtained by compensating the earth's magnetic force with an external magnet. Inasmuch, however, as the effect to be measured is not magnetic, it is better to obtain a small force of restitution by diminishing the moment of the suspended magnet rather than by diminishing the intensity of the field in which it works. In this way the zero will be less liable to be affected by accidental magnetic disturbances.

So far as I have tested it hitherto, the performance of the instrument is satisfactory. What strikes one most in its use is the enormous disproportion that it reveals between sounds which, when heard consecutively, appear to be of the same order of magnitude.

On the Circulation of Air Observed in Kundt's Tubes, and on Some Allied Acoustical Problems (1883)

[*Philosophical Transactions*, CLXXV, pp. 1–21, 1883]

Editorial Preface

In this paper the author discusses probably for the first time theoretically the phenomenon now known as acoustic streaming. The paper is too long for complete reproduction. We present the introduction and paragraph 3 relating to Kundt's tubes. In interpreting Rayleigh's analysis we must remember that he rarely employed the partial derivative notation, though his pages bristle with them. His fundamental symbols have the following physical meaning:

a = velocity of sound,

p = acoustic excess pressure,

ρ = excess density,

u, v = particle velocities in acoustical disturbance in the x and y direction respectively,

v, v' = shear and bulk viscosities respectively,

σ = acoustic condensation.log ρ/ρ_0

Acoustic streaming in the hands of modern bioacoustics investigators has led to important discoveries about the effect of sound on biological materials.

Experimenters in Acoustics have discovered more than one set of phenomena, apparently depending for their explanation upon the existence of regular currents of air resulting from vibratory motion, of which theory has as yet rendered no account. This is not, perhaps, a matter for surprise, when we consider that such currents, involving as they do *circulation* of the fluid, could not arise in the absence of friction, however great the extent of vibration. And even when we are prepared to include in our investigations the influence of friction, by which the motion of fluid in the neighbourhood of solid bodies may be greatly modified, we have no chance of reaching an explanation, if, as is usual, we limit ourselves to the supposition of infinitely small motion and neglect the squares and higher powers of the mathematical symbols by which it is expressed.

In the present paper three problems of this kind are considered, two of which are illustrative of phenomena observed by Faraday*. In these problems the fluid may be treated as incompressible. The more important of them relates to the currents generated over a vibrating plate, arranged as in Chladni's experiments. It was discovered by Savart that very fine powder does not collect itself at the nodal lines, as does sand in the production of Chladni's figures, but gathers itself into a cloud which, after hovering for a time, settles itself over the places of maximum vibration. This was traced by Faraday to the action of currents of air, rising from the plate at the places of maximum vibration, and falling back to it at the nodes. In a vacuum the phenomena observed by Savart do not take place, all kinds of powder collecting at the nodes. In the investigation of this, as of the other problems, the motion is supposed to take place in two dimensions.

It is probable that the colour phenomena observed by Sedley Taylor† on liquid films under the action of sonorous vibrations are to be referred to the operation of the aerial vortices here investigated. In a memoir on the colours of the soap-bubble‡, Brewster has described the peculiar arrangements of colour, accompanied by whirling motions, caused by the impact of a gentle current of air. In Mr Taylor's experiments the film probably divides itself into vibrating sections, associated with which will be aerial vortices reacting laterally upon the film.

The third problem relates to the air currents observed by Dvorak in a Kundt's tube, to which is apparently due the formation of the dust figures. In this case we are obliged to take into account the compressibility of the fluid.

* "On a Peculiar Class of Acoustical Figures; and on certain Forms assumed by groups of particles upon Vibrating Elastic Surfaces," *Phil. Trans.* 1831, p. 299.

†*Proc. Roy. Soc.* 1878.

‡*Edinburgh Transactions.* 1866-67.

§ 3. In the third problem, relating to Kundt's tubes, the fluid must be treated as compressible, as the motion is supposed to be approximately in one dimension, parallel (say) to x. The solution to a first approximation is merely an adaptation to two dimensions of the corresponding solution for a tube of revolution by Kirchhoff*, simplified by the neglect of the terms relating to the development and conduction of heat. It is probable that the solution to the second order would be practicable also for a tube of revolution, but for the sake of simplicity I have adhered to the case of two dimensions. The most important point in which the two problems are likely to differ can be investigated very simply, without a complete solution.

If we suppose $p = a^2\rho$, and write σ for $\log \rho - \log \rho_0$, the fundamental equations are

$$a^2 \frac{d\sigma}{dx} = -\frac{du}{dt} - u\frac{du}{dx} - v\frac{du}{dy} + \nu\nabla^2 u + \nu'\frac{d}{dx}\left(\frac{du}{dx} + \frac{dv}{dy}\right), \quad (56)$$

with a corresponding equation for v, and the equation of continuity,

$$\frac{du}{dx} + \frac{dv}{dy} + \frac{d\sigma}{dt} + u\frac{d\sigma}{dx} + v\frac{d\sigma}{dy} = 0. \quad (57)$$

Whatever may be the actual values of u and v, we may write

$$u = \frac{d\phi}{dx} + \frac{d\psi}{dy}, \qquad v = \frac{d\phi}{dy} - \frac{d\psi}{dx}, \quad (58)$$

in which

$$\nabla^2\phi = \frac{du}{dx} + \frac{dv}{dy}, \qquad \nabla^2\psi = \frac{du}{dy} - \frac{dv}{dx}. \quad (59)$$

From (56), (57),

$$\left(a^2 + \nu'\frac{d}{dt}\right)\frac{d\sigma}{dx} = -\frac{du}{dt} + \nu\nabla^2 u - u\frac{du}{dx} - v\frac{du}{dy}$$
$$- \nu'\frac{d}{dx}\left(u\frac{\vartheta d\sigma}{dx} + v\frac{d\sigma}{dy}\right), \quad (60)$$

---

* *Pogg. Ann.* t. CXXXIV, 1868.

$$\left(a^2 + v'\frac{d}{dt}\right)\frac{d\sigma}{dy} = -\frac{dv}{dt} + v\nabla^2 v - u\frac{dv}{dx} - v\frac{dv}{dy}\right)$$

$$- v'\frac{d}{dy}\left(u\frac{d\sigma}{dx} + v\frac{d\sigma}{dy}\right). \quad (61)$$

Again, from (60), (61),

$$\left(a^2 + v\frac{d}{dt} + v'\frac{d}{dt}\right)\nabla^2\sigma - \frac{d^2\sigma}{dt^2}$$

$$= \frac{d}{dt}\left(u\frac{d\sigma}{dx} + v\frac{d\sigma}{dy}\right) - (v + v')\nabla^2\left(u\frac{d\sigma}{dx} + v\frac{d\sigma}{dy}\right)$$

$$- \frac{d}{dx}\left(u\frac{du}{dx} + v\frac{du}{dy}\right) - \frac{d}{dy}\left(u\frac{dv}{dx} + v\frac{dv}{dy}\right). \quad (62)$$

For the first approximation the terms of the second order in u, v and σ are to be omitted. If we assume that as functions of t, all the periodic quantities are proportional to e^{int}, and write q for $a^2 + inv + inv'$, (62) becomes

$$q\nabla^2\sigma + n^2\sigma = 0 . \quad (63)$$

Now by (57), (59),

$$\nabla^2\phi = -in\sigma = iqn^{-1}\nabla^2\sigma,$$

so that

$$\phi = iqn^{-1}\sigma,*$$

and

$$u = \frac{iq}{n}\frac{d\sigma}{dx} + \frac{d\psi}{dy}, \qquad v = \frac{iq}{n}\frac{d\sigma}{dy} - \frac{d\psi}{dx}. \quad (64)$$

Substituting in (60), (61), with omission of terms of the second order, we get in view of (63),

$$(v\nabla^2 - in)\frac{d\psi}{dy} = 0 , \qquad (v\nabla^2 - in)\frac{d\psi}{dx} = 0 ,$$

whence

$$(v\nabla^2 - in)\psi = 0 . \quad (65)$$

* It is unnecessary to add a complementary function ϕ', satisfying $\nabla^2\phi'=0$, as the motion corresponding thereto may be regarded as covered by ψ.

If we eliminate σ directly from the fundamental equations (56), we get

$$\left(\nu\nabla^4 - \frac{d}{dt}\nabla^2\right)\psi = \frac{d}{dy}\left(u\frac{du}{dx} + v\frac{du}{dy}\right) - \frac{d}{dx}\left(u\frac{dv}{dx} + v\frac{dv}{dy}\right)$$

$$= \frac{d}{dy}(v\nabla^2\psi) + \frac{d}{dx}(u\nabla^2\psi)$$

$$= \left(\frac{du}{dx} + \frac{dv}{dy}\right)\nabla^2\psi + u\frac{d\nabla^2\psi}{dx} + v\frac{d\nabla^2\psi}{dy}. \tag{66}$$

If we now assume that as functions of x the quantities σ, ψ, &c., are proportional to e^{ikx}, equations (63), (65) may be written

$$(d^2/dy^2 - k''^2)\,\sigma = 0, \qquad \text{where } k''^2 = k^2 - n^2/q, \tag{67}$$

$$(d^2/dy^2 - k'^2)\,\psi = 0, \qquad \text{where } k'^2 = k^2 + in/\nu. \tag{68}$$

If the origin for y be in the middle between the two parallel boundaries, σ must be an even function of y, and ψ must be an odd function. Thus we may write

$$\sigma = A\cosh k''y\,.\,e^{int}e^{ikx}, \qquad \psi = B\sinh k'y\,.\,e^{int}e^{ikx}, \tag{69}$$

$$\left.\begin{array}{l} u = \left(-\dfrac{kq}{n}A\cosh k''y + k'B\sinh k'y\right)e^{int}e^{ikx} \\[2ex] v = \left(\dfrac{ik''q}{n}A\sinh k''y - ikB\sinh k'y\right)e^{int}e^{ikx} \end{array}\right\}. \tag{70}$$

If the fixed walls are situated at $y = \pm y_1$, u and v must vanish for these values of y. Eliminating from (70) the ratio of A to B, we get as the equation for determining k,

$$k^2\tanh k'y_1 = k'k''\tanh k''y_1\,, \tag{71}$$

in which k', k'' are given as functions of k by (67), (68). We now introduce further approximations dependent upon the assumption that the direct influence of friction extends through a layer whose thickness is a small fraction only of y_1. On this supposition k' is large, and k'' is small, so that we may put $\tanh k'y_1 = \pm 1$,

$\tanh k''y_1 = \pm k''y_1$. Equation (71) then becomes

$$k^2 = k'k''^2y_1, \tag{72}$$

or if we introduce the values of k', k'' from (67), (68),

$$k^2 = (k^2 - n^2/q)\, y_1\, \sqrt{(k^2 + in/v)}.$$

Since in/v is great, $k^2 = n^2/q = n^2/a^2$ approximately. Thus

$$k^2 = \frac{n^2}{q} + \frac{k^2}{y_1\, \sqrt{(k^2 + in/v)}} = \frac{n^2}{a^2}\left\{1 + \frac{1}{y_1\, \sqrt{(in/v)}}\right\},$$

and

$$k = \pm \frac{n}{a}\left\{1 + \frac{1-i}{2y_1\, \sqrt{(2n/v)}}\right\}. \tag{73}$$

If we write $k = k_1 + ik_2$,

$$k_1 = \pm \frac{n}{a}\left\{1 + \frac{\sqrt{(v/2n)}}{2y_1}\right\}, \qquad k_2 = \mp \frac{n}{a}\frac{\sqrt{(v/2n)}}{2y_1}, \tag{74}$$

which agrees with the result given in § 347 (11) of my book on the Theory of Sound.

In taking approximate forms for (70), we must distinguish which half of the symmetrical motion we contemplate. If we choose that for which y is *negative*, we replace $\cosh k'y$ and $\sinh k'y$ by $\frac{1}{2}e^{-k'y}$. For $\cosh k''y$ we may write unity, and for $\sinh k''y$ simply $k''y$. If we change the arbitrary multiplier so that the maximum value of u is unity, we have

$$u = (-1 + e^{-k'(y+y_1)})\, e^{ikx}\, e^{int},$$

$$v = \frac{ik}{k'}\left(\frac{y}{y_1} + e^{-k(y+y\,)}\right) e^{ikx}\, e^{int}, \tag{75}$$

in which, of course, u and v vanish when $y = -y_1$.

If in (75) we change k into $-k$, and then take the mean, we obtain

$$u = (-1 + e^{-k'(y+y_1)}) \cos kx\, e^{int},$$

$$v = -\frac{k}{k'}\left(\frac{y}{y_1} + e^{-k'(y+y_1)}\right) \sin kx\, e^{int}. \tag{76}$$

Although k is not absolutely a real quantity, we may consider it to be so with sufficient approximation for our purpose. If we write as before

$$k' = \sqrt{(n/2\nu)} \,.\, (1 + i) = \beta(1 + i),$$

we get from (76) in terms of real quantities

$$\left. \begin{aligned} u &= \cos kx \left[-\cos nt + e^{-\beta(y+y_1)} \cos \{nt - \beta(y + y_1)\} \right] \\ v &= -\frac{k}{\beta\sqrt{2}} \sin kx \left[\frac{y}{y_1} \cos (nt - \tfrac{1}{4}\pi) \right. \\ &\qquad \left. + e^{-\beta(y+y_1)} \cos\{nt - \tfrac{1}{4}\pi - \beta(y + y_1)\} \right] \end{aligned} \right\} . \quad (77)$$

It will shorten the expressions with which we have to deal if we measure y from the wall (on the negative side) instead of as hitherto from the plane of symmetry, for which purpose we must write y for $y + y_1$. Thus

$$\left. \begin{aligned} u &= \cos kx \{ -\cos nt + e^{-\beta y} \cos (nt - \beta y) \} \\ v &= \frac{k \sin kx}{\beta\sqrt{2}} \left\{ \frac{y_1 - y}{y_1} \cos (nt - \tfrac{1}{4}\pi) \right. \\ &\qquad \left. - e^{-\beta y} \cos (nt - \tfrac{1}{4}\pi - \beta y) \right\} \end{aligned} \right\} . \quad (78)$$

From (78) approximately

$$\nabla^2\psi = \beta\sqrt{2} \,.\, \cos kx \, e^{-\beta y} \sin (nt - \tfrac{1}{4}\pi - \beta y), \qquad (79)$$

$$\frac{du}{dx} + \frac{dv}{dy} = k \sin kx \cos nt, \qquad (80)$$

$$u \frac{d\nabla^2\psi}{dx} + v \frac{d\nabla^2\psi}{dy} = \tfrac{1}{2}k\beta \sin 2kx \, e^{-\beta y} (-\cos \beta y + e^{-\beta y}) \\ + \text{terms in } 2nt, \qquad (81)$$

$$\left(\frac{du}{dx} + \frac{dv}{dy} \right) \nabla^2\psi = -\tfrac{1}{4}k\beta \sin 2kx \, e^{-\beta y} (\sin \beta y + \cos \beta y) \\ + \text{terms in } 2nt. \qquad (82)$$

As in former problems the periodic terms in $2nt$ will be omitted.

For the non-periodic part of ψ of the second order, we have from (66)

$$\nabla^4\psi = -\frac{k\beta}{4\nu} \sin 2kx \, e^{-\beta y} \{\sin \beta y + 3 \cos \beta y - 2 e^{-\beta y}\}. \quad (83)$$

In this we identify ∇^4 with d^4/dy^4, so that

$$\psi = \frac{k \sin 2kx \, e^{-\beta y}}{16\nu\beta^3} \{\sin \beta y + 3 \cos \beta y + \tfrac{1}{2}e^{-\beta y}\}, \quad (84)$$

to which must be added a complementary function, satisfying $\nabla^4\psi = 0$, of the form

$$\psi = \frac{\sin 2kx}{16\nu\beta^3} \{A \sinh 2k(y_1 - y) + B(y_1 - y) \cosh 2k(y_1 - y)\}, \quad (85)$$

or as we may take it approximately, if y_1 be small compared with the wave-length λ,

$$\psi = \frac{k \sin 2kx}{16\nu\beta^3} \{A'(y_1 - y) + B'(y_1 - y)^3\}. \quad (86)$$

The value of σ to a second approximation would have to be investigated by means of (62). It will be composed of two parts, the first independent of t, the second a harmonic function of $2nt$. In calculating the part of $d\phi/dx$ independent of t from

$$\nabla^2\phi = -\frac{d\sigma}{dt} - u\frac{d\sigma}{dx} - v\frac{d\sigma}{dy},$$

we shall obtain nothing from $d\sigma/dt$. In the remaining terms on the right-hand side it will be sufficient to employ the values of u, v, σ of the first approximation. From

$$\frac{d\sigma}{dt} = -\frac{du}{dx} - \frac{dv}{dy},$$

in conjunction with (80), we get

$$\sigma = -(u_0/a) \sin kx \sin nt,$$

whence

$$\frac{d^2\phi}{d(\beta y)^2} = \frac{ku_0^2}{2a\beta^2} \cos^2 kx \, e^{-\beta y} \sin \beta y.$$

It is easily seen from this that the part of u resulting from $d\phi/dx$ is of order $k^2\beta^2$ in comparison with the part (87) resulting from ψ, and may be omitted.

Accordingly by (84), with introduction of the value of β and (in order to restore homogeneity) of u_0^2

$$u = - \frac{u_0^2 \sin 2kx \, e^{-\beta y}}{8a} \{4 \sin \beta y + 2 \cos \beta y + e^{-\beta y}\}, \qquad (87)$$

$$v = - \frac{2ku_0^2 \cos 2kx \, e^{-\beta y}}{8\beta a} \{\sin \beta y + 3 \cos \beta y + \tfrac{1}{2}e^{-\beta y}\}; \qquad (88)$$

and from (86)

$$u = - \frac{u_0^2 \sin 2kx}{8\beta a} \{A' + 3B'(y_1 - y)^2\}, \qquad (89)$$

$$v = - \frac{2ku_0^2 \cos 2kx}{8\beta a} \{A'(y_1 - y) + B'(y_1 - y)^3\}. \qquad (90)$$

When $y = 0$, the complete values of u and v, as given by the four last equations, must vanish. Determining in this way the arbitrary constants A' and B', we get as the complete values at any point,

$$u = - \frac{u_0^2 \sin 2kx}{8a} \left\{ e^{-\beta y} (4 \sin \beta y + 2 \cos \beta y \right.$$
$$\left. + e^{-\beta y}) + \tfrac{3}{2} - \tfrac{9}{2} \frac{(y_1 - y)^2}{y_1^2} \right\}, \qquad (91)$$

$$v = - \frac{2ku_0^2 \cos 2kx}{8\beta a} \left\{ e^{-\beta y} (\sin \beta y + 3 \cos \beta y + \tfrac{1}{2}e^{-\beta y}) \right.$$
$$\left. + \tfrac{3}{2}\beta(y_1 - y) - \tfrac{3}{2}\beta \frac{(y_1 - y)^3}{y_1^2} \right\}. \qquad (92)$$

Outside the thin film of air immediately influenced by the friction we may put $e^{-\beta y} = 0$, and then

$$u = -\frac{3u_0^2 \sin 2kx}{16a}\left\{1 - 3\frac{(y_1 - y)^2}{y_1^2}\right\}, \tag{93}$$

$$v = -\frac{3u_0^2 \, 2k \cos 2kx}{16a}\left\{y_1 - y - \frac{(y_1 - y)^3}{y_1^2}\right\}. \tag{94}$$

From (93) we see that u changes sign as we pass from the boundary $y = 0$ to the plane of symmetry $y = y_1$, the critical value of y being $y_1(1 - \sqrt{\tfrac{1}{3}})$, or $\cdot423y_1$.

The principal motion being $u = -u_0 \cos kx \cos nt$, the loops correspond to $kx = 0, \pi, 2\pi, \ldots$, and the nodes correspond to $\tfrac{1}{2}\pi, \tfrac{3}{2}\pi, \ldots$. Thus v is positive at the nodes and negative at the loops, vanishing of course in either case both at the wall $y = 0$, and at the plane of symmetry $y = y_1$.

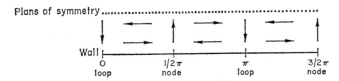

To obtain the mean velocities of the *particles* parallel to x, we must make an addition to u, as in the former problems.

In the present case the mean value of

$$\frac{du}{dx}\xi + \frac{du}{dy}\eta = \frac{u_0^2 \sin 2kx \, e^{-\beta y}}{4a}\left\{e^{-\beta y} - \cos \beta y\right\},$$

so that

$$u' = -\frac{u_0^2 \sin 2kx}{8a}\left\{e^{-\beta y}\,(4 \sin \beta y + 3e^{-\beta y}) \right.$$
$$\left. + \tfrac{3}{2} - \tfrac{9}{2}\frac{(y_1 - y)^2}{y_1^2}\right\}. \tag{95}$$

When βy is small,

$$u' = -\frac{u_0^2 \sin 2kx}{8a}\left\{-2\beta y + \ldots\right\}. \tag{96}$$

Inside the frictional layer the motion is in the same direction as just beyond it.

We have seen that the width of the direct current along the wall is ·423 y_1, and that of the return current (measured up to the plane of symmetry) is ·577 y_1, so that the direct current is distinctly narrower than the return current. This will be still more the case in a tube of circular section. The point under consideration depends only upon a complementary function analogous to (86), and is so simple that it may be worth while to investigate it.

The equation for ψ is

$$\left(\frac{d^2}{dr^2} - \frac{1}{r}\frac{d}{dr} - 4k^2\right)^2 \psi = 0, \tag{97}$$

but if we suppose that the radius of the tube is small in comparison with λ, k^2 may be omitted. The general solution is

$$\psi = \{A + Br^2 + B'r^2 \log r + Cr^4\} \sin 2kx, \tag{98}$$

so that

$$u = \frac{1}{r}\frac{d\psi}{dr} = \{2B + B'(2\log r + 1) + 4Cr^2\} \sin 2kx,$$

whence $B' = 0$, by the condition at $r = 0$. Again,

$$v = -\frac{1}{r}\frac{d\psi}{dx} = -2k\{Ar^{-1} + Br + Cr^3\} \cos 2kx,$$

whence $A = 0$.

We may take therefore

$$u = \{2B + 4Cr^2\} \sin 2kx, \quad v = -2k\{Br + Cr^3\} \cos 2kx \tag{99}$$

If $v = 0$, when $r = R$, $B + CR^2 = 0$, and

$$u = 2C(2r^2 - R^2) \sin 2kx. \tag{100}$$

Thus u vanishes, when

$$r = \frac{R}{\sqrt{2}} = ·707\,R, \quad R - r = ·293\,R.$$

The direct current is thus limited to an annulus of thickness ·293 R, the return current occupying the whole interior, and having therefore a diameter of

$$2 \times ·707\,R = 1·414\,R.$$

Presidential Address to the
British Association's Montreal Meeting (1884)

[*British Association Report*, pp. 1–23, Montreal, 1884

Editorial Preface

Rayleigh's presidential address at the British Association's Montreal meeting in 1884 marked an epoch in his professional career. Having served his five years' tenure as Cavendish Professor at Cambridge as successor to Maxwell, he had established himself as one of the leading British physicists of his day. What he had to say on this occasion reflected his estimate of the then state of physical research. Though in no sense a complete survey (for this even in his day was impracticable) it possesses considerable historical interest today and justifies the presentation here of certain sections.

Rayleigh began by calling attention to the innovation involved in holding a meeting of the British Association outside of the United Kingdom and followed this with some remarks about Sir W. Siemens, a distinguished member of the Association who had died since the previous meeting. Selections from the more substantive parts of his address follow.

As it is now several years since your presidential chair has been occupied by a professed physicist, it may naturally be expected that I should attempt some record of recent progress in that branch of science, if indeed such a term be applicable. For it is one of the difficulties of the task that subjects as distinct as Mechanics, Electricity, Heat, Optics and Acoustics, to say nothing of Astronomy and Meteorology, are included under Physics. Any one of these may well occupy the life-long attention of a man of science, and to be thoroughly conversant with all of them is more than can be expected of any one individual, and is probably incompatible with the devotion of much time and energy to the actual advancement of knowledge. Not that I would complain of the association sanctioned by common parlance. A sound knowledge of at least the principles of general physics is necessary to the cultivation of any department. The predominance of the sense of sight as the medium of communication with the outer world, brings with it dependence upon the science of optics; and there is hardly a branch of science in which the effects of *temperature* have not (often without much success) to be reckoned with. Besides, the neglected borderland between two branches of knowledge is often that which best repays cultivation, or, to use a metaphor of Maxwell's, the greatest benefits may be derived from a cross fertilisation of the sciences. The wealth of material is an evil only from the point of view of one of whom too much may be expected. Another difficulty incident to the task, which must be faced but cannot be overcome, is that of estimating rightly the value, and even the correctness, of recent work. It is not always that which seems at first the most important that proves in the end to be so. The history of science teems with examples of discoveries which attracted little notice at the time, but afterwards have taken root downwards and borne much fruit upwards.

One of the most striking advances of recent years is in the production and application of electricity upon a large scale—a subject to which I have already had occasion to allude in connection with the work of Sir W. Siemens. The dynamo machine is indeed founded upon discoveries of Faraday now more than half a century old; but it has required the protracted labours of many inventors to bring it to its present high degree of efficiency. Looking back at the matter, it seems strange that progress should have been so slow. I do not refer to details of design, the elaboration of which must always, I suppose, require the experience of actual work to indicate what parts are structurally weaker than they should be, or are exposed to undue wear and tear. But with regard to the main features of the problem, it would almost seem as if the difficulty lay in want of faith. Long ago it was recognised that electricity derived from chemical action is (on a large scale) too expensive a source of mechanical power, notwithstanding the fact that (as proved by Joule in 1846) the conversion of electrical into mechanical work can be effected with great economy. From this it is an evident consequence that electricity may advantageously be obtained from mechanical power; and one cannot help thinking that if the fact had been borne steadily in mind, the development of the dynamo might have been much more rapid. But discoveries and inventions are apt to appear obvious when regarded from the standpoint of accomplished fact; and I draw attention to the matter only to point the moral that we do well to push the attack persistently when we can be sure beforehand that the obstacles to be overcome are only difficulties of contrivance, and that we are not vainly fighting unawares against a law of Nature.

The present development of electricity on a large scale depends, however, almost as much upon the incandescent lamp as upon the dynamo. The success of these lamps demands a very perfect vacuum—not more than about one-millionth of the normal quantity of air should remain,—and it is interesting to recall that, twenty years ago, such vacua were rare even in the laboratory of the physicist. It is pretty safe to say that these wonderful results would never have been accomplished had practical applications alone been in view. The way was prepared by an army of scientific men whose main object was the advancement of knowledge, and who could scarcely have imagined that the processes which they elaborated would soon be in use on a commercial scale and entrusted to the hands of ordinary workmen.

The requirements of practice react in the most healthy manner upon scientific electricity. Just as in former days the science received a stimulus from the application to telegraphy, under which everything relating to measurement on a small scale acquired an importance and development for which we might otherwise have had long to wait, so now the requirements of electric lighting are giving rise to a new development of the art of measurement upon a large scale, which cannot fail to prove of scientific as well as practical importance. Mere change of scale may not at first appear a very important matter, but it is surprising how much modification it entails in the instruments, and in the processes of measurement. For instance, the resistance coils on which the electrician relies in dealing with currents whose maximum is a fraction of an ampére, fail altogether when it becomes a question of hundreds, not to say thousands, of ampères.

The powerful currents, which are now at command, constitute almost a new weapon in the hands of the physicist. Effects, which in old days were rare and difficult of observation, may now be produced at will on the most conspicuous scale. Consider for a moment Faraday's great discovery of the "Magnetisation of Light," which Tyndall likens to the Weisshorn among mountains, as high, beautiful, and alone. This judgment (in which I fully concur) relates to the scientific aspect of the discovery, for to the eye of sense nothing could have been more insignificant. It is even possible that it might have eluded altogether the penetration of Faraday, had he not been provided with a special quality of very heavy glass. At the present day these effects may be produced upon a scale that would have delighted their discoverer, a rotation of the plane of polarization through 180° being perfectly feasible. With the aid of modern appliances, Kundt and Röntgen in Germany, and H. Becquerel in France, have detected the rotation in gases and vapours, where, on account of its extreme smallness, it had previously escaped notice.

During the last few years much interest has been felt in the reduction to an absolute standard of measurements of electromotive force, current, resistance, etc., and to this end many laborious investigations have been undertaken. The subject is one that has engaged a good deal of my own attention, and I should naturally have felt inclined to dilate upon it, but that I feel it to be too abstruse and special to be dealt with in detail upon an occasion like the present. As regards resistance, I will merely remind you that the recent determinations have shown a so greatly improved agreement, that the Conference of Electricians assembled at Paris, in May, have felt themselves justified in defining the ohm for practical use as the resistance of a column of mercury of 0° C., one square millimetre in section, and 106 centimetres in length—a definition differing by a little more than one per cent.

from that arrived at twenty years ago by a committee of this Association.

A standard of resistance once determined upon can be embodied in a "resistance coil," and copied without much trouble, and with great accuracy. But in order to complete the electrical system, a second standard of some kind is necessary, and this is not so easily embodied in a permanent form. It might conveniently consist of a standard galvanic cell, capable of being prepared in a definite manner, whose electro-motive force is once for all determined. Unfortunately, most of the batteries in ordinary use are for one reason or another unsuitable for this purpose, but the cell introduced by Mr Latimer Clark, in which the metals are zinc in contact with saturated zinc sulphate and pure mercury in contact with mercurous sulphate, appears to give satisfactory results. According to my measurements, the electro-motive force of this cell is 1·435 theoretical volts.

We may also conveniently express the second absolute electrical measurement necessary to the completion of the system by taking advantage of Faraday's law, that the quantity of metal decomposed in an electrolytic cell is proportional to the whole quantity of electricity that passes. The best metal for the purpose is silver, deposited from a solution of the nitrate or of the chlorate. The results recently obtained by Professor Kohlrausch and by myself are in very good agreement, and the conclusion that one ampére flowing for one hour decomposes 4·025 grains of silver, can hardly be in error by more than a thousandth part. This number being known, the silver voltameter gives a ready and very accurate method of measuring currents of intensity, varying from $\frac{1}{10}$ ampére to four or five ampéres.

The beautiful and mysterious phenomena attending the discharge of electricity in nearly vacuous spaces have been investigated and in some degree explained by De La Rue, Crookes, Schuster, Moulton, and the lamented Spottiswoode, as well as by various able foreign experimenters. In a recent research Crookes has sought the origin of a bright citron-coloured band in the phosphorescent spectrum of certain earths, and after encountering difficulties and anomalies of a most bewildering kind, has succeeded in proving that it is due to yttrium, an element much more widely distributed than had been supposed. A conclusion like this is stated in a few words, but those only who have undergone similar experience are likely to appreciate the skill and perseverance of which it is the final reward.

A remarkable observation by Hall of Baltimore, from which it appeared that the flow of electricity in a conducting sheet was disturbed by magnetic force, has been the subject of much discussion. Mr Shelford Bidwell has brought forward experiments tending to prove that the effect is of a secondary character, due in the first instance to the mechanical force operating upon the conductor of an electric current when situated in a powerful magnetic field. Mr Bidwell's view agrees in the main with Mr Hall's division of the metals into two groups according to the direction of the effect.

Without doubt the most important achievement of the older generation of scientific men has been the establishment and application of the great laws of Thermo-dynamics, or, as it is often called, the Mechanical Theory of Heat. The first law, which asserts that heat and mechanical work can be transformed one into the other at a certain fixed rate, is now well understood by every student of physics, and the number expressing the mechanical equivalent of heat resulting from the experiments of Joule, has been confirmed by the researches of others, and especially of Rowland. But the second law, which practically is even more important than the first, is only now beginning to receive the full appreciation due to it. One reason of this may be found in a not unnatural confusion of ideas. Words do not always lend themselves readily to the demands that are made upon them by a growing science, and I think that the almost unavoidable use of the word equivalent in the statement of the first law is partly responsible for the little attention that is given to the second. For the second law so far contradicts the usual statement of the first, as to assert that equivalents of heat and work are not of equal value. While work can always be converted into heat, heat can only be converted into work under certain limitations. For every practical purpose the work is worth the most, and when we speak of equivalents, we use the word in the same sort of special sense as that in which chemists speak of equivalents of gold and iron. The second law teaches us that the real value of heat, as a source of mechanical power, depends upon the temperature of the body in which it resides; the hotter the body in relation to its surroundings, the more available the heat.

In order to see the relations which obtain between the first and the second law of Thermo-dynamics, it is only necessary for us to glance at the theory of the steam-engine. Not many years ago calculations were plentiful, demonstrating the inefficiency of the steam-engine on the basis of a comparison of the work actually got out of the engine with the mechanical equivalent of the heat supplied to the boiler. Such calculations took into account only the first law of Thermo-dynamics, which deals with the equivalents of heat and work, and have very little bearing upon the practical question of efficiency, which requires us to have regard also to the second law. According to that law the fraction of the total energy which can be converted into work depends upon the relative temperatures of the boiler and condenser; and it is, therefore, manifest that, as the temperature of the boiler cannot be raised indefinitely, it is impossible to utilise all the energy which, according to the first law of Thermo-dynamics, is resident in the coal.

On a sounder view of the matter, the efficiency of the steam-engine is found to be so high, that there is no great margin remaining for improvement. The higher initial temperature possible in the gas-engine opens out much wider possibilities, and many good judges look forward to a time when the steam-engine will have to give way to its younger rival.

To return to the theoretical question, we may say with Sir W. Thomson, that though energy cannot be destroyed, it ever tends to be dissipated, or to pass from more available to less available forms. No one who has grasped this principle can fail to recognise its immense importance in the system of the Universe. Every change—chemical, thermal, or mechanical—which takes place, or can take place, in Nature does so, at the cost of a certain amount of available energy. If, therefore, we wish to inquire whether or not a proposed transformation can take place, the question to be considered is whether its occurrence would involve dissipation of energy. If not, the transformation is (under the circumstances of the case) absolutely excluded. Some years ago, in a lecture at the Royal Institution*, I endeavoured to draw the attention of chemists to the importance of the principle of dissipation in relation to their science, pointing out the error of the usual assumption that a general criterion is to be found in respect of the development of heat. For example, the solution of a salt in water is, if I may be allowed the phrase, a downhill transformation. It involves dissipation of energy, and can therefore go forward; but in many cases it is associated with the absorption rather than with the development of heat. I am glad to take advantage of the present opportunity in order to repeat my recommendation, with an emphasis justified by actual achievement. The foundations laid by Thomson now bear an edifice of no mean proportions, thanks to the labours of several physicists, among whom must be especially mentioned Willard Gibbs and Helmholz. The former has elaborated a theory of the equilibrium of heterogeneous substances, wide in its principles, and we cannot doubt far-reaching in its consequences. In a series of masterly papers Helmholtz has developed the conception of *free energy* with very important applications to the theory of the galvanic cell. He points out that the mere tendency to solution bears in some cases no small proportion to the affinities more usually reckoned chemical, and contributes largely to the total electromotive force. Also in our own country Dr Alder Wright has published some valuable experiments relating to the subject.

The nature of gaseous viscosity, as due to the diffusion of momentum, has been made clear by the theoretical and experimental researches of Maxwell. A flat disc moving in its own plane

*[Art. 35.]

between two parallel solid surfaces is impeded by the necessity of shearing the intervening layers of gas, and the magnitude of the hindrance is proportional to the velocity of the motion and to the viscosity of the gas, so that under similar circumstances this effect may be taken as a measure, or rather definition, of the viscosity. From the dynamical theory of gases, to the development of which he contributed so much, Maxwell drew the startling conclusion that the viscosity of a gas should be independent of its density,— that within wide limits the resistance to the moving disc should be scarcely diminished by pumping out the gas, so as to form a partial vacuum. Experiment fully confirmed this theoretical anticipation,—one of the most remarkable to be found in the whole history of science, and proved that the swinging disc was retarded by the gas, as much when the barometer stood at half an inch as when it stood at thirty inches. It was obvious, of course, that the law must have a limit, that at a certain point of exhaustion the gas must begin to lose its power; and I remember discussing with Maxwell, soon after the publication of his experiments, the whereabouts of the point at which the gas would cease to produce its ordinary effect. His apparatus, however, was quite unsuited for high degrees of exhaustion, and the failure of the law was first observed by Kundt and Warburg, at pressures below 1 mm. of mercury. Subsequently the matter has been thoroughly examined by Crookes, who extended his observations to the highest degrees of exhaustion as measured by MacLeod's gauge. Perhaps the most remarkable results relate to hydrogen. From the atmospheric pressure of 760 mm. down to about $\frac{1}{2}$ mm. of mercury the viscosity is sensibly constant. From this point to the highest vacua, in which less than one-millionth of the original gas remains, the coefficient of viscosity drops down gradually to a small fraction of its original value. In these vacua Mr Crookes regards the gas as having assumed a different, ultra-gaseous, condition; but we must remember that the phenomena have relation to the other circumstances of the case, especially the dimensions of the vessel, as well as to the condition of the gas.

Such an achievement as the prediction of Maxwell's law of viscosity has, of course, drawn increased attention to the dynamical theory of gases. The success which has attended the theory in the hands of Clausius, Maxwell, Boltzmann and other mathematicians, not only in relation to viscosity, but over a large part of the entire field of our knowledge of gases, proves that some of its fundamental postulates are in harmony with the reality of Nature. At the same time, it presents serious difficulties; and we cannot but feel that while the electrical and optical properties of gases remain out of relation to the theory, no final judgment is possible. The growth of experimental knowledge may be trusted to clear up many doubtful points, and a younger generation of theorists will bring to bear improved mathematical weapons. In the meantime we may fairly congratulate ourselves on the possession of a guide which has already conducted us to a position which could hardly otherwise have been attained.

In Optics attention has naturally centred upon the spectrum. The mystery attaching to the invisible rays lying beyond the red has been fathomed to an extent that, a few years ago, would have seemed almost impossible. By the use of special photographic methods Abney has mapped out the peculiarities of this region with such success that our knowledge of it begins to be comparable with that of the parts visible to the eye. Equally important work has been done by Langley, using a refined invention of his own based upon the principle of Siemens' pyrometer. This instrument measures the actual energy of the radiation, and thus expresses the effects of various parts of the spectrum upon a common scale, independent of the properties of the eye and of sensitive photographic preparations. Interesting results have also been obtained by Becquerel, whose method is founded upon a curious action of the ultra-red rays in enfeebling the light emitted by phosphorescent substances. One of the most startling of Langley's conclusions relates to the influence of the atmosphere in modifying the quality of solar light. By the comparison of observations made through varying thicknesses of air, he shows that the atmospheric absorption tells most upon the light of high refrangibility; so that, to an eye situated outside the atmosphere, the sun would present a decidedly bluish tint. It would be interesting to compare the experimental numbers with the law of scattering of light by small particles given some years ago as the result of theory*. The demonstration by Langley of the inadequacy of Cauchy's law of dispersion to represent the relation between refrangibility and wave-length in the lower part of the spectrum must have an important bearing upon optical theory.

The investigation of the relation of the visible and ultra-violet spectrum to various forms of matter has occupied the attention of a host of able workers, among whom none have been more successful than my colleagues at Cambridge, Professors Liveing and Dewar. The subject is too large both for the occasion and for the individual, and I must pass it by. But, as more closely related to Optics proper, I cannot resist recalling to your notice a beautiful application of the idea of Doppler to the discrimination of the origin of certain lines observed in the solar spectrum. If a vibrating body have a general motion of approach or recession, the waves emitted from it reach the observer with a frequency which in the first case exceeds, and in the second case falls short of, the real frequency of the vibrations themselves. The consequence is that, if a glowing gas be in motion in the line of sight, the spectral lines are thereby displaced from the position that they would occupy were the gas at rest—a principle which, in the hands of Huggins and others, has led to a determination of the motion of certain fixed stars relatively to the solar system. But the sun is itself in rotation, and thus the position of a solar spectral line is slightly different according as the light comes from the advancing or from the retreating limb. This displacement was, I believe, first observed by Thollon; but what I desire now to draw attention to is the application of it by Cornu to determine whether a line is of solar or atmospheric origin. For this purpose a small image of the sun is thrown upon the slit of the spectroscope, and caused to

* [See Art. 8.]

vibrate two or three times a second, in such a manner that the light entering the instrument comes alternately from the advancing and retreating limbs. Under these circumstances a line due to absorption within the sun appears to tremble, as the result of slight alternately opposite displacements. But if the seat of the absorption be in the atmosphere, it is a matter of indifference from what part of the sun the light originally proceeds, and the line maintains its position in spite of the oscillation of the image upon the slit of the spectroscope. In this way Cornu was able to make a discrimination which can only otherwise be effected by a difficult comparison of appearances under various solar altitudes.

The great optical constant, the velocity of light, has been the subject of three distinct investigations by Cornu, Michelson, and Forbes. As may be supposed, the matter is of no ordinary difficulty, and it is therefore not surprising that the agreement should be less decided than could be wished. From their observations, which were made by a modification of Fizeau's method of the toothed wheel, Young and Forbes drew the conclusion that the velocity of light *in vacuo* varies from colour to colour, to such an extent that the velocity of blue light is nearly two per cent. greater than that of red light. Such a variation is quite opposed to existing theoretical notions, and could only be accepted on the strongest evidence. Mr Michelson, whose method (that of Foucault) is well suited to bring into prominence a variation of velocity with wave-length, informs me that he has recently repeated his experiments with special reference to the point in question, and has arrived at the conclusion that no variation exists comparable with that asserted by Young and Forbes. The actual velocity differs little from that found from his first series of experiments, and may be taken to be 299,800 kilometres per second.

The beautiful inventions of the telephone and the phonograph, although in the main dependent upon principles long since established, have imparted a new interest to the study of Acoustics.

The former, apart from its uses in every-day life, has become in the hands of its inventor, Graham Bell, and of Hughes, an instrument of first-class scientific importance. The theory of its action is still in some respects obscure, as is shown by the comparative failure of the many attempts to improve it. In connection with some explanations that have been offered, we do well to remember that molecular changes in solid masses are inaudible in themselves, and can only be manifested to our ears by the generation of a to and fro motion of the external surface extending over a sensible area. If the surface of a solid remains undisturbed, our ears can tell us nothing of what goes on in the interior.

In theoretical acoustics progress has been steadily maintained, and many phenomena, which were obscure twenty or thirty years ago, have since received adequate explanation. If some important practical questions remain unsolved, one reason is that they have not yet been definitely stated. Almost everything in connection with the ordinary use of our senses presents peculiar difficulties to scientific investigation. Some kinds of information with regard to their surroundings are of such paramount importance to successive generations of living beings, that they have learned to interpret indications which, from a physical point of view, are of the slenderest character. Every day we are in the habit of recognising, without much difficulty, the quarter from which a sound proceeds, but by what steps we attain that end has not yet been satisfactorily explained. It has been proved* that when proper precautions are taken we are unable to distinguish whether a pure tone (as from a vibrating tuning-fork held over a suitable resonator) comes to us from in front or from behind. This is what might have been expected from an *à priori* point of view; but what would not have been expected is that with almost any other sort of sound, from a clap of the hands to the clearest vowel sound, the discrimination is not only possible but easy and instinctive. In these cases it does not appear how the possession of two ears helps us, though there is some evidence that it does; and even when sounds come to use from the right or left, the

* [See Art. 40 and 46. See also p. 100 of present work.]

explanation of the ready discrimination which is then possible with pure tones, is not so easy as might at first appear. We should be inclined to think that the sound was heard much more loudly with the ear that is turned towards than with the ear that is turned from it, and that in this way the direction was recognised. But if we try the experiment, we find that, at any rate with notes near the middle of the musical scale, the difference of loudness is by no means so very great. The wave-lengths of such notes are long enough in relation to the dimensions of the head to forbid the formation of anything like a sound shadow in which the averted ear might be sheltered.

In concluding this imperfect survey of recent progress in physics, I must warn you emphatically that much of great importance has been passed over altogether. I should have liked to speak to you of those far-reaching speculations, especially associated with the name of Maxwell, in which light is regarded as a disturbance in an electro-magnetic medium. Indeed, at one time, I had thought of taking the scientific work of Maxwell as the principal theme of this address. But, like most men of genius, Maxwell delighted in questions too obscure and difficult for hasty treatment, and thus much of his work could hardly be considered upon such an occasion as the present. His biography has recently been published, and should be read by all who are interested in science and in scientific men. His many-sided character, the quaintness of his humour, the penetration of his intellect, his simple but deep religious feeling, the affection between son and father, the devotion of husband to wife, all combine to form a rare and fascinating picture. To estimate rightly his influence upon the present state of science, we must regard not only the work that he executed himself, important as that was, but also the ideas and the spirit which he communicated to others. Speaking for myself as one who in a special sense entered into his labours, I should find it difficult to express adequately my feeling of obligation. The impress of his thoughts may be recognised in much of the best work of the present time. As a teacher and examiner he was well acquainted with the almost universal tendency of un-instructed minds to elevate phrases above things: to refer, for example, to the principle of the conservation of energy for an explanation of the persistent rotation of a fly-wheel, almost in the style of the doctor in *Le Malade Imaginaire*, who explains the fact that opium sends you to sleep by its soporific virtue. Maxwell's endeavour was always to keep the facts in the foreground, and to his influence, in conjunction with that of Thomson and Helmholtz, is largely due that elimination of unnecessary hypothesis which is one of the distinguishing characteristics of the science of the present day.

In speaking unfavourably of superfluous hypothesis, let me not be misunderstood. Science is nothing without generalisations. Detached and ill-assorted facts are only raw material, and in the absence of a theoretical solvent, have but little nutritive value. At the present time and in some departments, the accumulation of material is so rapid that there is danger of indigestion. By a fiction as remarkable as any to be found in law, what has once been published, even though it be in the Russian language, is usually spoken of as "known," and it is often forgotten that the re-discovery in the library may be a more difficult and uncertain process than the first discovery in the laboratory. In this matter we are greatly dependent upon annual reports and abstracts, issued principally in Germany, without which the search for the dis-coveries of a little-known author would be well-nigh hopeless. Much useful work has been done in this direction in connection with our Association. Such critical reports as those upon Hydro-dynamics, upon Tides, and upon Spectroscopy, guide the in-vestigator to the points most requiring attention, and in discussing past achievements contribute in no small degree to future progress. But though good work has been done, much yet remains to do.

If, as is sometimes supposed, science consisted in nothing but the laborious accumulation of facts, it would soon come to a stand-still, crushed, as it were, under its own weight. The sug-gestion of a new idea, or the detection of a law, supersedes much that had previously been a burden upon the memory, and by introducing order and coherence facilitates the retention of the remainder in an available form. Those who are acquainted with the writings of the older electricians will understand my meaning when I instance the discovery of Ohm's law as a step by which the science was rendered easier to understand and to remember. Two processes are thus at work side by side, the reception of new material and the digestion and assimilation of the old; and as both are essential, we may spare ourselves the discussion of their relative importance. One remark, however, should be made. The work which deserves, but I am afraid does not always receive, the most credit is that in which discovery and explanation go hand in hand, in which not only are new facts presented, but their relation to old ones is pointed out.

In making oneself acquainted with what has been done in any subject, it is good policy to consult first the writers of highest general reputation. Although in scientific matters we should aim at independent judgment, and not rely too much upon authority, it remains true that a good deal must often be taken upon trust. Occasionally an observation is so simple and easily repeated, that it scarcely matters from whom it proceeds; but as a rule it can hardly carry full weight when put forward by a novice whose care and judgment there has been no opportunity of testing, and whose irresponsibility may tempt him to "take shots," as it is called. Those who have had experience in accurate work know how easy it would be to save time and trouble by omitting precautions and passing over discrepancies, and yet, even without dishonest intention, to convey the impression of conscientious attention to details. Although the most careful and experienced cannot hope to escape occasional mistakes, the effective value of this kind of work depends much upon the reputation of the individual responsible for it.

In estimating the present position and prospects of experimental science, there is good ground for encouragement. The multiplication of laboratories gives to the younger generation opportunities such as have never existed before, and which excite the envy of those who have had to learn in middle life much that now forms

F

part of an undergraduate course. As to the management of such institutions there is room for a healthy difference of opinion. For many kinds of original work, especially in connection with accurate measurement, there is need of expensive apparatus; and it is often difficult to persuade a student to do his best with imperfect appliances when he knows that by other means a better result could be attained with greater facility. Nevertheless, it seems to me important to discourage too great reliance upon the instrument maker. Much of the best original work has been done with the homeliest appliances; and the endeavour to turn to the best account the means that may be at hand develops ingenuity and resource more than the most elaborate determinations with ready-made instruments. There is danger otherwise that the experimental education of a plodding student should be too mechanical and artificial, so that he is puzzled by small changes of apparatus much as many school-boys are puzzled by a transposition of the letters in a diagram of Euclid.

Without encroaching upon grounds appertaining to the theologian and the philosopher, the domain of natural sciences is surely broad enough to satisfy the wildest ambition of its devotees. In other departments of human life and interest, true progress is rather an article of faith than a rational belief; but in science a retrograde movement is, from the nature of the case, almost impossible. Increasing knowledge brings with it increasing power, and great as are the triumphs of the present century, we may well believe that they are but a foretaste of what discovery and invention have yet in store for mankind. Encouraged by the thought that our labours cannot be thrown away, let us redouble our efforts in the noble struggle. In the Old World and in the New, recruits must be enlisted to fill the place of those whose work is done. Happy should I be if, through this visit of the Association, or by any words of mine, a larger measure of the youthful activity of the West could be drawn into this service. The work may be hard, and the discipline severe; but the interest never fails, and great is the privilege of achievement.

On Waves Propagated Along the Plane Surface of an Elastic Solid (1885)

[*Proceedings of the London Mathematical Society*, XVII, pp. 4–11, 1885]

Editorial Preface

This is the celebrated paper in which was introduced the study of surface waves in elastic solids. Such waves have received the name, Rayleigh waves, and have proved to be of great importance in modern investigations of mechanical radiation in solids. In examining the analysis note that μ is the shear modulus of elasticity and λ, the so-called Lamé coefficient, is equal to the bulk modulus minus two-thirds the shear modulus.

This article is reproduced in its entirety.

It is proposed to investigate the behaviour of waves upon the plane free surface of an infinite homogeneous isotropic elastic solid, their character being such that the disturbance is confined to a superficial region, of thickness comparable with the wavelength. The case is thus analogous to that of deep-water waves, only that the potential energy here depends upon elastic resilience instead of upon gravity*.

Denoting the displacements by α, β, γ, and the dilation by θ, we have the usual equations

$$\rho \frac{d^2\alpha}{dt^2} = (\lambda + \mu) \frac{d\theta}{dx} + \mu \nabla^2 \alpha, \quad \&c., \tag{1}$$

in which

$$\theta = \frac{d\alpha}{dx} + \frac{d\beta}{dy} + \frac{d\gamma}{dz}. \tag{2}$$

---

* The statical problem of the deformation of an elastic solid by a harmonic application of pressure to its surface has been treated by Prof. G. Darwin, *Phil. Mag.* Dec. 1882. Jan. 1886. See also Camb. Math. Trip. Ex. Jan. 20, 1875, Question IV.

If a, β, γ all vary as e^{ipt}, equations (1) become

$$(\lambda + \mu)\frac{d\theta}{dx} + \mu\nabla^2 a + \rho p^2 a = 0, \quad \&c. \tag{3}$$

Differentiating equations (3) in order with respect to x, y, z, and adding, we get

$$(\nabla^2 + h^2)\,\theta = 0, \tag{4}$$

in which

$$h^2 = \rho p^2/(\lambda + 2\mu). \tag{5}$$

Again, if we put

$$k^2 = \rho p^2/\mu, \tag{6}$$

equations (3) take the form

$$(\nabla^2 + k^2)\,a = \left(1 - \frac{k^2}{h^2}\right)\frac{d\theta}{dx}, \quad \&c. \tag{7}$$

A particular solution of (7) is*

$$a = -\frac{1}{h^2}\frac{d\theta}{dx}, \quad \beta = -\frac{1}{h^2}\frac{d\theta}{dy}, \quad \gamma = -\frac{1}{h^2}\frac{d\theta}{dz}; \tag{8}$$

in order to complete which it is only necessary to add complementary terms u, v, w satisfying the system of equations.

$$(\nabla^2 + k^2)\,u = 0, \quad (\nabla^2 + k^2)\,v = 0, \quad (\nabla^2 + k^2)\,w = 0, \tag{9}$$

$$\frac{du}{dx} + \frac{dv}{dy} + \frac{dw}{dz} = 0. \tag{10}$$

For the purposes of the present problem we take the free surface as the plane $z = 0$, and assume that, as functions of x and y, the displacements are proportional to e^{ifx}, e^{igy}. Thus (4) takes the form

$$(d^2/dz^2 + h^2 - f^2 - g^2)\,\theta = 0;$$

so that

$$\theta = Pe^{-rz} + Qe^{+rz}, \tag{11}$$

* Lamb on the Vibrations of an Elastic Sphere, *Math. Soc. Proc.* May 1882.

where
$$r^2 = f^2 + g^2 - h^2. \tag{12}$$

In (11), r is supposed to be real; otherwise the dilatation would penetrate to an indefinite depth. For the same reason, we must retain only that term (say the first) for which the exponent is negative within the solid*. Thus $Q = 0$, and we will write for brevity $P = 1$, or rather $P = e^{ipt}\, e^{ifx}\, e^{igy}$; but the exponential factors may often be omitted without risk of confusion, so that we may take

$$\theta = e^{-rz}. \tag{13}$$

At the same time the particular solution becomes

$$a = -\frac{if}{h^2}e^{-rz}, \quad \beta = -\frac{ig}{h^2}e^{-rz}, \quad \gamma = \frac{r}{h^2}e^{-rz}. \tag{14}$$

For the complementary terms, which must also contain e^{ifx}, e^{igy} as factors, equations (9) become

$$(d^2/dz^2 + k^2 - f^2 - g^2)\, u = 0, \quad \&c.; \tag{15}$$

whence, as before, on the assumption that the disturbance is limited to a superficial stratum,

$$u = Ae^{-sz}, \quad v = Be^{-sz}, \quad w = Ce^{-sz}, \tag{16}$$

where
$$s^2 = f^2 + g^2 - k^2. \tag{17}$$

In order to satisfy (10), the coefficients in (16) must be subject to the relation

$$ifA + igB - sC = 0. \tag{18}$$

The complete values of a, β, γ may now be written

$$a = -\frac{if}{h^2}e^{-rz} + Ae^{-sz}, \quad \beta = -\frac{ig}{h^2}e^{-rz} + Be^{-sz},$$

$$\gamma = \frac{r}{h^2}e^{-rz} + Ce^{-sz}, \tag{19}$$

---

* By discarding these restrictions we may deduce the complete solution applicable to a plate, bounded by parallel plane free surfaces; but I have not obtained any results which seem worthy of quotation.

in which A, B, C are subject to (18); and the next step is to express the boundary conditions for the free surface. The two components of tangential stress must vanish, when $z = 0$, and these are proportional to

$$\frac{d\beta}{dz} + \frac{d\gamma}{dy}, \quad \frac{d\gamma}{dx} + \frac{d\alpha}{dz}$$

respectively. Hence

$$sB = \frac{2igr}{h^2} + igC, \quad sA = \frac{2ifr}{h^2} + ifC. \tag{20}$$

Substituting from (20) in (18), we find

$$C(s^2 + f^2 + g^2) h^2 + 2r(f^2 + g^2) = 0. \tag{21}$$

We have still to introduce the condition that the normal traction is zero at the surface. We have, in general,

$$N_3 = \lambda\theta + 2\mu \frac{dy}{dz};$$

or, if we express λ in terms of μ, h, k,

$$N_3 = \mu \left\{ \left(\frac{k^2}{h^2} - 2 \right) \theta + 2 \frac{d\gamma}{dz} \right\};$$

so that the condition is

$$k^2 - 2h^2 - 2(+ r^2 + h^2 sC) = 0,$$

or, on substitution for r^2 of its value from (12),

$$k^2 - 2(f^2 + g^2) - 2h^2 sC = 0. \tag{22}$$

By eliminating C between (21) and (22), we obtain the equation by which the time of vibration is determined as a function of the wavelengths and of the properties of the solid. It is

$$\{k^2 - 2(f^2 + g^2)\} \{s^2 + f^2 + g^2\} + 4rs(f^2 + g^2) = 0,$$

or, by (17),

$$\{2(f^2 + g^2) - k^2\}^2 = 4rs(f^2 + g^2). \tag{23}$$

If we square (23), and introduce the values of r^2 and s^2 from (12), (17), we get

$$\{2(f^2 + g^2) - k^2\}^4 = 16(f^2 + g^2)^2(f^2 + g^2 - h^2)(f^2 + g^2 - k^2).$$

As f and g occur here only in the combination $(f^2 + g^2)$, a quantity homogeneous with h^2 and k^2, we may conveniently replace $(f^2 + g^2)$ by unity.
Thus

$$k^8 - 8k^6 + 24k^4 - 16k^2 - 16h^2k^2 + 16h^2 = 0. \qquad (24)$$

Since the ratio $h^2 : k^2$ is known, this equation reduces to a cubic and determines the value of either quantity.

If the solid be incompressible ($\lambda = \infty$), $h^2 = 0$, and the equation becomes

$$k^6 - 8k^4 + 24k^2 - 16 = 0. \qquad (25)$$

The real root of (25) is found to be ·91275, and the equation may be written

$$(k^2 - ·91275)(k^4 - 7·08725k^2 + 17·5311) = 0.$$

The general theory of vibrations of stable systems forbids us to look for complex values of k^2, as solutions of our problem, though it would at first sight appear possible with them to satisfy the prescribed conditions by taking such roots of (12), (17), as would make the *real* parts of the exponents in e^{-rz}, e^{-sz} negative. But, referring back to (23), which we write in the form

$$(2 - k^2)^2 = 4rs,$$

or, in the present case of incompressibility, by putting $r = 1$,

$$(2 - k^2)^2 = 4s,$$

we see that we are not really free to choose the sign of s. In fact, from the complex values of k^2, viz., $3·5436 \pm 2·2301i$, we find

$$4s = -2·7431 \pm 6·8846i;$$

so that the real part of s is of the opposite sign to r, and therefore e^{-rz}, e^{-sz} do not both diminish without limit as we penetrate further and further into the solid.

Dismissing then the complex values, we have, in the case of incompressibility, the single solution

$$k^2 = \frac{\rho p^2}{\mu} = \cdot 91275 \, (f^2 + g^2). \tag{26}$$

From (19), (20), (21), we get in general

$$h^2 a = if \left\{ -e^{-rz} + \frac{2rs}{s^2 + f^2 + g^2} e^{-sz} \right\}, \tag{27}$$

$$h^2 \beta = ig \left\{ -e^{-rz} + \frac{2rs}{s^2 + f^2 + g^2} e^{-sz} \right\}, \tag{28}$$

$$h^2 \gamma = r \left\{ +e^{-rz} - \frac{2(f^2 + g^2)}{s^2 + f^2 + g^2} e^{-sz} \right\}. \tag{29}$$

In the case of incompressibility, we have k^2 given by (26), and

$$r^2 = f^2 + g^2, \quad s^2 = \cdot 08725 \, (f^2 + g^2).$$

Hence

$$\begin{aligned} h^2 a &= if \, \{-e^{-rz} + \cdot 5433 e^{-sz}\} \, e^{ipt} \, e^{ifx} \, e^{igy} \\ h^2 \beta &= ig \, \{-e^{-rz} + \cdot 5433 e^{-sz}\} \, e^{ipt} \, e^{ifx} \, e^{igy} \\ h^2 \gamma &= \sqrt{(f^2 + g^2)} \, \{e^{-rz} - 1 \cdot 840 e^{-sz}\} \, e^{ipt} \, e^{ifx} \, e^{igy} \end{aligned} \right\}. \tag{30}$$

If we suppose the motion to be in two dimensions only, we may put $g = 0$; so that $\beta = 0$, and

$$\begin{aligned} h^2 a / f &= i \, \{-e^{-fz} + \cdot 5433 e^{-sz}\} \, e^{ipt} \, e^{ifx} \\ h^2 \gamma / f &= \quad \{ e^{-fz} - 1 \cdot 840 e^{-sz}\} \, e^{ipt} \, e^{ifx} \end{aligned} \right\}, \tag{31}$$

in which

$$k = \cdot 9554 f, \qquad s = \cdot 2954 f. \tag{32}$$

For a progressive wave we may take simply the real parts of (31). Thus

$$\begin{aligned} h^2 a / f &= (e^{-fz} - \cdot 5433 e^{-sz}) \sin \, (pt + fx) \\ h^2 \gamma / f &= (e^{-fz} - 1 \cdot 840 e^{-sz}) \cos \, (pt + fx) \end{aligned} \right\}. \tag{33}$$

The velocity of propagation is p/f, or $\cdot 9554 \sqrt{(\mu/\rho)}$, in which $\sqrt{(\mu/\rho)}$ is the velocity of purely transverse plane waves. The surface waves now under consideration move, therefore, rather more slowly than these.

From (32), (33), we see that a vanishes for all values of x and t when $e^{(s-f)z} = \cdot5433$, i.e., when $fz = \cdot8659$. Thus, if λ' be the wave-length $(2\pi/f)$, the horizontal motion vanishes at a depth equal to $\cdot1378\lambda'$. On the other hand, there is no finite depth at which the vertical motion vanishes.

To find the motion at the surface itself, we have only to put $z = 0$ in (33). We may drop at the same time the constant multiplier (h^2/f) which has no present significance. Accordingly,

$$a = \cdot4567 \sin(pt + fx), \qquad \gamma = -\cdot840 \cos(pt + fx), \qquad (34)$$

showing that the motion takes place in elliptic orbits, whose vertical axis is nearly the double of the horizontal axis.

The expressions for stationary vibrations may be obtained from (30) by addition to the similar equations obtained by changing the sign of p, and similar operations with respect to f and g. Dropping an arbitrary multiplier, we may write

$$\left.\begin{array}{l} a = -f \left\{-e^{-rz} + \cdot5433e^{-sz}\right\} \cos pt \sin fx \cos gy \\ \beta = -g \left\{-e^{-rz} + \cdot5433e^{-sz}\right\} \cos pt \cos fx \sin gy \\ \gamma = r \left\{+e^{-rz} - 1\cdot840e^{-sz}\right\} \cos pt \cos fx \cos gy \end{array}\right\}, \qquad (35)$$

in which

$$r = \sqrt{(f^2 + g^2)}, \qquad s = \cdot2954\sqrt{(f^2 + g^2)}. \qquad (36)$$

As before, the horizontal motion vanishes at a depth such that

$$\sqrt{(f^2 + g^2)}\, z = \cdot8659.$$

We will now examine how far the numerical results are affected when we take into account the finite compressibility of all natural bodies. The ratio of the elastic constants is often stated by means of the number expressing the ratio of lateral contraction to longitudinal extension when a bar of the material is trained by forces applied to its ends. According to a theory now generally discarded, this ratio (σ) would be $\frac{1}{4}$; a number which, however, is not far from the truth for a variety of materials, including the principal metals. In the extreme case of incompressibility σ is $\frac{1}{2}$, and there seems to be no theoretical reason why σ should not have any value between this and -1*.

The accompanying table will give an idea of the progress of the values of $k^2/(f^2 + g^2)$ as dependent upon λ/μ, or upon σ. It will be observed that the value diminishes continuously with λ, in accordance with a general principle†.

λ	σ	h^2/k^2	$k^2/(f + g^2)$	$k/\sqrt(f^2 + g^2)$
∞	$\frac{1}{2}$	0	·9127	·9554
μ	$\frac{1}{4}$	$\frac{1}{3}$	·8453	·9194
0	0	$\frac{1}{2}$	·7640	·8741
$-\frac{2}{3}\mu$	-1	$\frac{3}{4}$	·4746	·6896

As an example of finite compressibility, we will consider further the second case of the table. From (12), (17),

$$r^2 = ·7182\,(f^2 + g^2), \qquad r = ·8475\sqrt{(f^2 + g^2)},$$
$$s^2 = ·1547\,(f^2 + g^2), \qquad s = ·3933\sqrt{(f^2 + g^2)}.$$

Hence, from (27), (28), (29), in correspondence with (30), we have

$$\left. \begin{aligned} h^2\alpha &= if\,\{-e^{-rz} + ·5773e^{-sz}\}\,e^{ipt}\,e^{ifx}\,e^{igy} \\ h^2\beta &= ig\,\{-e^{-rz} + ·5773e^{-sz}\}\,e^{ipt}\,e^{ifx}\,e^{igy} \\ h^2\gamma &= ·8475\sqrt{(f^2 + g^2)}\,\{e^{-rz} - 1·7320e^{-sz}\}\,e^{ipt}\,e^{ifx}\,e^{igy} \end{aligned} \right\}. \quad (37)$$

For a progressive wave in two dimensions, we shall have

$$\left. \begin{aligned} h^2\alpha/f &= (e^{-rz} - ·5773e^{-sz})\sin\,(pt + fx) \\ h^2\gamma/f &= (·8475e^{-rz} - 1·4679e^{-sz})\cos\,(pt + fx) \end{aligned} \right\}. \quad (38)$$

* Prof. Lamb, in his able paper, seems to regard all negative values of σ as excluded *a priori*. But the necessary and sufficient conditions of stability are merely that the resistance to compression $(\lambda + \frac{2}{3}\mu)$ and the resistance to shearing (μ) should be positive. In the second extreme case of a medium which resists shear, but does not resist compression, $\lambda = -\frac{2}{3}\mu$, and $\sigma = -1$. The velocity of a dilatational wave is then $\frac{4}{3}$ of that of a distortional plane wave. (Green, *Camb. Trans.* 1838.) The general value of σ is $\lambda/(2\lambda + 2\mu)$.

† *Math. Soc. Proc.* June 1873, vol. IV, p. 359 [Art. 21]. *Theory of Sound*, t. I p. 85. Lamb, *loc. cit.* p. 202.

At the surface,

$$h^2\alpha/f = +\cdot4227 \sin (pt + fx) \left.\right\}$$
$$h^2\gamma/f = -\cdot6204 \cos (pt + fx) \left.\right\} \tag{39}$$

so that the vertical axes of the elliptic orbits are about half as great again as the horizontal axes.

It is proper to remark that the vibrations here considered are covered by the general theory of spherical vibrations given by Lamb in the paper referred to. But it would probably be as difficult, if not more difficult, to deduce the conclusions of the present paper from the analytical expressions of the general theory, as to obtain them independently. It is not improbable that the surface waves here investigated play an important part in earthquakes, and in the collision of elastic solids. Diverging in two dimensions only, they must acquire at a great distance from the source a continually increasing preponderance.

On the Physics of Media
that are Composed of Free and Perfectly
Elastic Molecules in a State of Motion* (1892)

[*Phil. Trans.* A, CLXXXIII, pp. 1–5, 1892]

Editorial Preface

This is Rayleigh's introduction to the printing for the first time of the
1845 memoir of the Scottish engineer J. J. Waterston, in which he established
the theoretical basis for the molecular theory of gases. Rayleigh's comments
are an indication of his interest in the history of physics and his desire to do
justice after some 50 years to the pioneer work of a practically unknown
investigator.

The publication of this paper after nearly half a century
demands a word of explanation; and the opportunity may be
taken to point out in what respects the received theory of gases
had been anticipated by Waterston, and to offer some suggestions
as to the origin of certain errors and deficiencies in his views.

So far as I am aware, the paper, though always accessible in
the Archives of the Royal Society, has remained absolutely
unnoticed. Most unfortunately the abstract printed at the time
(*Roy. Soc. Proc.* 1846, Vol. v, p. 604; here reprinted as Appendix
I.) gave no adequate idea of the scope of the memoir, and still
less of the nature of the results arrived at. The deficiency was
in some degree supplied by a short account in the *Report of the
British Association* for 1851 (here reprinted as Appendix II.),
where is distinctly stated the law, which was afterwards to become
so famous, of the equality of the kinetic energies of different
molecules at the same temperature.

* [From an Introduction to a Memoir, entitled as above, by J. J. Waterston,
received Dec. 11, 1845, read March 5, 1846.]

My own attention was attracted in the first instance to Waterston's work upon the connection between molecular forces and the latent heat of evaporation, and thence to a paper in the *Philosophical Magazine* for 1858, "On the Theory of Sound." He there alludes to the theory of gases under consideration as having been started by Herapath in 1821, and he proceeds:—

"Mr Herapath unfortunately assumed heat or temperature to be represented by the simple ratio of the velocity instead of the square of the velocity—being in this apparently led astray by the definition of motion generally received—and thus was baffled in his attempts to reconcile his theory with observation. If we make this change in Mr Herapath's definition of heat or temperature, viz., that it is proportional to the *vis viva*, or square velocity of the moving particle, not to the momentum, or simple ratio of the velocity, we can without much difficulty deduce, not only the primary laws of elastic fluids, but also the other physical properties of gases enumerated above in the third objection to Newton's hypothesis. In the Archives of the Royal Society for 1845–1846, there is paper 'On the Physics of Media that consists of perfectly Elastic Molecules in a State of Motion,' which contains the synthetical reasoning upon which the demonstration of these matters rests. The velocity of sound is therein deduced to be equal to the velocity acquired in falling through three-fourths of a uniform atmosphere. This theory does not take account of the size of the molecules. It assumes that no time is lost at the impact, and that if the impacts produce rotatory motion, the *vis viva* thus invested bears a constant ratio to the rectilineal *vis viva*, so as not to require separate consideration. It also does not take account of the probable internal motion of composite molecules; yet the results so closely accord with observation in every part of the subject as to leave no doubt that Mr Herapath's idea of the physical constitution of gases approximates closely to the truth. M. Krönig appears to have entered upon the subject in an independent manner, and arrives at the same result; M. Clausius, too, as we learn from his paper 'On the Nature of the Motion we call Heat' (*Phil. Mag.* Vol. XIV, 1857, p. 108)."

Impressed with the above passage and with the general ingenuity and soundness of Waterston's views, I took the first opportunity of consulting the Archives, and saw at once that the memoir justified the large claims made for it, and that it marks an immense advance in the direction of the now generally received theory. The omission to publish it at the time was a misfortune, which probably retarded the development of the subject by ten or fifteen years. It is singular that Waterston appears to have advanced no claim for subsequent publication, whether in the Transactions of the Society, or through some other channel. At any time since 1860 reference would naturally have been made to Maxwell, and it cannot be doubted that he would have at once recommended that everything possible should be done to atone for the original failure of appreciation.

It is difficult to put oneself in imagination into the position of the reader of 1845, and one can understand that the substance of the memoir should have appeared speculative and that its mathematical style should have failed to attract. But it is startling to find a referee expressing the opinion that "the paper is nothing but nonsense, unfit even for reading before the Society." Another remarks "that the whole investigation is confessedly founded on a principle entirely hypothetical, from which it is the object to deduce a mathematical representation of the phenomena of elastic media. It exhibits much skill and many remarkable accordances with the general facts, as well as numerical values furnished by observation. . . . The original principle itself involves an assumption which seems to me very difficult to admit, and by no means a satisfactory basis for a mathematical theory, viz., that the elasticity of a medium is to be measured by supposing its molecules in vertical motion, and making a succession of impacts against an elastic gravitating plane." These remarks are not here quoted with the idea of reflecting upon the judgment of the referee, who was one of the best qualified authorities of the day, and evidently devoted to a most difficult task his careful attention; but rather with the view of throwing light upon the attitude then assumed by men of science in regard to this question, and in order to point a moral. The history of this paper suggests that highly speculative investigations, especially by an unknown author, are best brought before the world through some other channel than a scientific society, which naturally hesitates to admit into its printed records matter of uncertain value. Perhaps one may go further and say that a young author who believes himself capable of great things would usually do well to secure the favourable recognition of the scientific world by work whose scope is limited, and whose value is easily judged, before embarking upon higher flights.

One circumstance which may have told unfavourably upon the reception of Waterston's paper is that he mentions no predecessors. Had he put forward his investigation as a development of the theory of D. Bernoulli, a referee might have hesitated to call it nonsense. It is probable, however, that Waterston was unacquainted with Bernoulli's work, and doubtful whether at that time he knew that Herapath had to some extent foreshadowed similar views.

At the present time the interest of Waterston's paper can, of course, be little more than historical. What strikes one most is the marvellous courage with which he attacked questions, some of which even now present serious difficulties. To say that he was not always successful is only to deny his claim to rank among the very foremost theorists of all ages. The character of the advance to be dated from this paper will be at once understood when it is realised that Waterston was the first to introduce into the theory the conception that heat and temperature are to be measured by *vis viva*. This enabled him at a stroke to complete Bernoulli's explanation of pressure by showing the accordance of the hypothetical medium with the law of Dalton and Gay-Lussac. In the second section the great feature is the statement (VII.), that "in mixed media the mean square molecular velocity is inversely proportional to the specific weight of the molecules." The proof which Waterston gave is doubtless not satisfactory; but the same may be said of that advanced by Maxwell fifteen years later. The law of Avogadro follows at once, as well as that of Graham relative to diffusion. Since the law of equal energies was actually published in 1851, there can be no hesitation, I think, in attaching Waterston's name to it. The attainment of correct results in the third section, dealing with adiabatic expansion, was only prevented by a slip of calculation.

In a few important respects Waterston stopped short. There is no indication, so far as I can see, that he recognised any other form of motion, or energy, than the translatory motion, though this is sometimes spoken of as vibratory. In this matter the priority in a wider view rests with Clausius. According to Waterston the ratio of specific heats should be (as for mercury vapour) 1·67 in all cases. Again, although he was well aware that the molecular velocity cannot be constant, there is no anticipation of the law of distribution of velocities established by Maxwell.

A large part of the paper deals with chemistry, and shows that his views upon that subject also were much in advance of those generally held at the time. . . .

With the exception of some corrections relating merely to stops and spelling the paper is here reproduced exactly as it stands in the author's manuscript.—Dec. 1891.

[1901. It may be added that Waterston's memoir contains the first calculation of the molecular velocity, and further that it points out the relation of this velocity to the velocity of sound. The earliest actual *publication* of such a calculation is that of Joule, who gives for the velocity of hydrogen molecules at 0°C. 6055 feet per second (*Manchester Memoirs*, Vol. IX, p. 107, Oct. 1848; *Phil. Mag.* Ser. 4, Vol. XIV, p. 211; Joule's *Scientific Papers*, Vol. I, p. 295), thus anticipating by eight or nine years the first paper of Clausius (*Pogg. Ann.* 1857), to whom priority is often erroneously ascribed.]

Density of Nitrogen (1892)

[*Nature*, XLVI, pp. 512, 513, 1892]

Editorial Preface

The historical interest of this paper is very great, since here Rayleigh expresses publicly for the first time his puzzlement over the apparent inconsistency in the results of his density measurements of nitrogen obtained from the atmosphere on the one hand and from nitrogenous compounds on the other. He had for some time been engaged in precision measurements of density of the standard diatomic gases for the purpose of checking on atomic weight determinations. The anomaly presented by the results for nitrogen was, of course, the first step in the discovery and isolation of argon. Comments on the ultimate significance of this paper in connection with the problem of priority in the discovery of argon have already been made in Part II of this volume.

I am much puzzled by some recent results as to the density of nitrogen, and shall be obliged if any of your chemical readers can offer suggestions as to the cause. According to two methods of preparation I obtain quite distinct values. The relative difference, amounting to about 1/1000 part, is small in itself; but it lies entirely outside the errors of experiment, and can only be attributed to a variation in the character of the gas.

In the first method the oxygen of atmospheric air is removed in the ordinary way by metallic copper, itself reduced by hydrogen from the oxide. The air, freed from CO_2 by potash, gives up its oxygen to copper heated in hard glass over a large Bunsen, and *then* passes over about a foot of red-hot copper in a furnace. This tube was used merely as an indicator, and the copper in it remained bright throughout. The gas then passed through a wash-bottle containing sulphuric acid, thence again through the furnace over *copper oxide*, and finally over sulphuric acid, potash and phosphoric anhydride.

In the second method of preparation, suggested to me by Prof. Ramsay, everything remained unchanged, except that the *first* tube of hot copper was replaced by a wash-bottle containing liquid *ammonia*, through which air was allowed to bubble. The ammonia method is very convenient, but the nitrogen obtained by means of it was 1/1000 part lighter than the nitrogen of the first method. The question is, to what is the discrepancy due?

The first nitrogen would be too heavy, if it contained residual oxygen. But on this hypothesis, something like 1 per cent. would be required. I could detect none whatever by means of alkaline pyrogallate. It may be remarked that the density of the nitrogen agrees closely with that recently obtained by Leduc using the same method of preparation.

On the other hand, can the ammonia-made nitrogen be too light from the presence of impurity? There are not many gases lighter than nitrogen, and the absence of hydrogen, ammonia, and water seems to be fully secured. On the whole it seemed the more probable supposition that the impurity was hydrogen, which in this degree of dilution escaped the action of the copper oxide. But a special experiment seems to exclude this explanation.

Into nitrogen prepared by the first method, but before its passage into the furnace tubes, one or two thousandths by volumes of hydrogen were introduced. To effect this in a uniform manner the gas was made to bubble through a small hydrogen generator, which would be set in action under its own electro-motive force by closing an external contact. The rate of hydrogen production was determined by a suitable galvanometer enclosed in the circuit. But the introduction of hydrogen had not the smallest effect upon the density, showing that the copper oxide was capable of performing the part desired of it.

Is it possible that the difference is independent of impurity, the nitrogen itself being to some extent in a different (dissociated) state?

I ought to have mentioned that during the fillings of the globe, the rate of passage of gas was very uniform, and about 2/3 litre per hour.

Argon (1895)

[*Royal Institution Proceedings*, xiv, pp. 524–538, Ap. 1895]

Editorial Preface

This paper is reproduced in full not only because of the interest in the discovery of argon, the most spectacular of Rayleigh's achievements, but also because it provides a good example of his style of lecturing at the Royal Institution, where he gave many demonstration lectures. The lecture also sheds interesting light on Rayleigh's public attitude toward his collaboration with William Ramsay in the discovery.

It is some three or four years since I had the honour of lecturing here one Friday evening upon the densities of oxygen and hydrogen gases, and upon the conclusions that might be drawn from the results. It is not necessary, therefore, that I should trouble you to-night with any detail as to the method by which gases can be accurately weighed. I must take that as known, merely mentioning that it is substantially the same as is used by all investigators nowadays, and introduced more than fifty years ago by Regnault. It was not until after that lecture that I turned my attention to nitrogen; and in the first instance I employed a method of preparing the gas which originated with Mr Vernon Harcourt, of Oxford. In this method the oxygen of ordinary atmospheric air is got rid of with the aid of ammonia. Air is bubbled through liquid ammonia, and then passed through a red-hot tube. In its passage the oxygen of the air combines with the hydrogen of the ammonia, all the oxygen being in that way burnt up and converted into water. The excess of ammonia is subsequently absorbed with acid, and the water by ordinary desiccating agents. That method is very convenient; and, when I had obtained a few concordant results by means of it, I thought that the work was complete, and that the weight of nitrogen was satisfactorily determined. But then I reflected that it is always advisable to employ more than one method, and that the method that I had used—Mr Vernon Harcourt's method—was not that which had been used by any of those who had preceded me in weighing nitrogen. The usual method consists in absorbing the oxygen of air by means of red-hot copper; and I thought that I ought at least to give that method a trial, fully expecting to obtain forthwith a value in harmony with that already afforded by the ammonia method. The result, however, proved otherwise. The gas obtained by the copper method, as I may call it, proved to be one-thousandth part heavier than that obtained by the ammonia method; and, on repetition, that difference was only brought out more clearly. This was about three years ago. In order, if possible, to get further light upon a discrepancy which puzzled me very much, and which, at that time, I regarded only with disgust and impatience, I published a letter in *Nature** inviting criticisms from chemists who might be interested in such questions. I obtained various useful suggestions, but none going to the root of the matter. Several persons who wrote to me privately were inclined to think that the explanation was to be sought in a partial dissociation of the nitrogen derived from ammonia. For, before going further, I ought to explain that, in the nitrogen obtained by the ammonia method, some—about a seventh part—is derived from the ammonia, the larger part, however, being derived as usual from the atmosphere. If the chemically derived nitrogen were partly dissociated into its component atoms, then the lightness of the gas so prepared would be explained.

The next step in the enquiry was, if possible, to exaggerate the discrepancy. One's instinct at first is to try to get rid of a discrepancy, but I believe that experience shows such an endeavour to be a mistake. What one ought to do is to magnify a small discrepancy with a view to finding out the explanation; and, as it appeared in the present case that the root of the discrepancy lay

* [Art. 197.]

in the fact that part of the nitrogen prepared by the ammonia method was nitrogen out of ammonia, although the greater part remained of common origin in both cases, the application of the principle suggested a trial of the weight of nitrogen obtained wholly from ammonia. This could easily be done by substituting pure oxygen for atmospheric air in the ammonia method, so that the whole, instead of only a part, of the nitrogen collected should be derived from the ammonia itself. The discrepancy was at once magnified some five times. The nitrogen so obtained from ammonia proved to be about one-half per cent. lighter than nitrogen obtained in the ordinary way from the atmosphere, and which I may call for brevity "atmospheric" nitrogen.

That result stood out pretty sharply from the first; but it was necessary to confirm it by comparison with nitrogen chemically derived in other ways. The table before you gives a summary of such results, the numbers being the weights in grams actually contained under standard conditions in the globe employed.

ATMOSPHERIC NITROGEN

By hot copper (1892)	2·3103
By hot iron (1893)	2·3100
By ferrous hydrate (1894)	2·3102
	Mean 2·3102

CHEMICAL NITROGEN

From nitric oxide	2·3001
From nitrous oxide	2·2990
From ammonium nitrite purified at a red heat	2·2987
From urea	2·2985
From ammonium nitrite purified in the cold	2·2987
	Mean 2·2990

The difference is about 11 milligrams, or about one-half per cent.; and it was sufficient to prove conclusively that the two kinds of nitrogen—the chemically derived nitrogen and the atmospheric nitrogen—differed in weight, and therefore, of course, in quality, for some reason hitherto unknown.

I need not spend time in explaining the various precautions

that were necessary in order to establish surely that conclusion. One had to be on one's guard against impurities, especially against the presence of hydrogen, which might seriously lighten any gas in which it was contained. I believe, however, that the precautions taken were sufficient to exclude all questions of that sort, and the result, which I published about this time last year*, stood sharply out, that the nitrogen obtained from chemical sources was different from the nitrogen obtained from the air.

Well, that difference, admitting it to be established, was sufficient to show that some hitherto unknown gas is involved in the matter. It might be that the new gas was dissociated nitrogen, contained in that which was too light, the chemical nitrogen—and at first that was the explanation to which I leaned; but certain experiments went a long way to discourage such a supposition. In the first place, chemical evidence—and in this matter I am greatly dependent upon the kindness of chemical friends—tends to show that, even if ordinary nitrogen could be dissociated at all into its component atoms, such atoms would not be likely to enjoy any very long continued existence. Even ozone goes slowly back to the more normal state of oxygen; and it was thought that dissociated nitrogen would have even a greater tendency to revert to the normal condition. The experiment suggested by that remark was as follows—to keep chemical nitrogen—the too light nitrogen which might be supposed to contain dissociated molecules—for a good while, and to examine whether it changed in density. Of course it would be useless to shut up gas in a globe and weigh it, and then, after an interval, to weigh it again, for there would be no opportunity for any change of weight to occur, even although the gas within the globe had undergone some chemical alteration. It is necessary to re-establish the standard conditions of temperature and pressure which are always understood when we speak of filling a globe with gas, for I need hardly say that filling a globe with gas is but a figure of speech. Everything depends upon the temperature and pressure at which you work. However, that obvious point being borne in mind, it was

* [Art. 210.]

proved by experiment that the gas did not change in weight by standing for eight months—a result tending to show that the abnormal lightness was not the consequence of dissociation.

Further experiments were tried upon the action of the silent electric discharge—both upon the atmospheric nitrogen and upon the chemically derived nitrogen—but neither of them seemed to be sensibly affected by such treatment; so that, altogether, the balance of evidence seemed to incline against the hypothesis of abnormal lightness in the chemically derived nitrogen being due to dissociation, and to suggest strongly, as almost the only possible alternative, that there must be in atmospheric nitrogen some constituent heavier than true nitrogen.

At that point the question arose, What was the evidence that all the so-called nitrogen of the atmosphere was of one quality? And I remember—I think it was about this time last year, or a little earlier—putting the question to my colleague, Professor Dewar. His answer was that he doubted whether anything material had been done upon the matter since the time of Cavendish, and that I had better refer to Cavendish's original paper. That advice I quickly followed, and I was rather surprised to find that Cavendish had himself put this question quite as sharply as I could put it. Translated from the old-fashioned phraseology connected with the theory of phlogiston, his question was whether the inert ingredient of the air is really all of one kind; whether all the nitrogen of the air is really the same as the nitrogen of nitre. Cavendish not only asked himself this question, but he endeavoured to answer it by an appeal to experiment.

I should like to show you Cavendish's experiment in something like its original form. He inverted a U-tube filled with mercury, the legs standing in two separate mercury cups. He then passed up, so as to stand above the mercury, a mixture of nitrogen, or of air, and oxygen; and he caused an electric current from a frictional electrical machine like the one I have before me to pass from the mercury in the one leg to the mercury in the other, giving sparks across the intervening column of air. I do not propose to use a frictional machine to-night, but I will substitute for it one giving electricity of the same quality of the construction introduced by Mr Wimshurst, of which we have a fine specimen in the Institution. It stands just outside the door of the theatre, and will supply an electric current along insulated wires, leading to the mercury cups; and, if we are successful, we shall cause sparks to pass through the small length of air included above the columns of mercury. There they are; and after a little time you will notice that the mercury rises, indicating that the gas is sensibly absorbed under the influence of the sparks and of a piece of potash floating on the mercury. It was by that means that Cavendish established his great discovery of the nature of the inert ingredient in the atmosphere, which we now call nitrogen; and, as I have said, Cavendish himself proposed the question, as distinctly as we can do, Is this inert ingredient all of one kind? and he proceeded to test that question. He found, after days and weeks of protracted experiment, that, for the most part, the nitrogen of the atmosphere was absorbed in this manner, and converted into nitrous acid; but that there was a small residue remaining after prolonged treatment with sparks, and a final absorption of the residual oxygen. That residue amounted to about $\frac{1}{120}$ part of the nitrogen taken; and Cavendish draws the conclusion that, if there be more than one inert ingredient in the atmosphere, at any rate the second ingredient is not contained to a greater extent than $\frac{1}{120}$ part.

I must not wait too long over the experiment. Mr Gordon tells me that a certain amount of contraction has already occurred; and if we project the ∪ upon the screen, we shall be able to verify the fact. It is only a question of time for the greater part of the gas to be taken up, as we have proved by preliminary experiments.

In what I have to say from this point onwards, I must be understood as speaking as much on behalf of Professor Ramsay as for myself. At the first, the work which we did was to a certain extent independent. Afterwards we worked in concert, and all that we have published in our joint names must be regarded as being equally the work of both of us. But, of course, Professor

Ramsay must not be held responsible for any chemical blunder into which I may stumble to-night.

By his work and by mine the heavier ingredient in atmospheric nitrogen which was the origin of the discrepancy in the densities has been isolated, and we have given it the name of "argon". For this purpose we may use the original method of Cavendish, with the advantages of modern appliances. We can procure more powerful electric sparks than any which Cavendish could command by the use of the ordinary Ruhmkorff coil stimulated by a battery of Grove cells; and it is possible so to obtain evidence of the existence of argon. The oxidation of nitrogen by that method goes on pretty quickly. If you put some ordinary air, or, better still, a mixture of air and oxygen, in a tube in which electric sparks are made to pass for a certain time, then in looking through the tube, you observe the well-known reddish-orange fumes of the oxides of nitrogen. I will not take up time in going through the experiment, but will merely exhibit a tube already prepared (image on screen).

One can work more efficiently by employing the alternate currents from dynamo machines which are now at our command. In this Institution we have the advantage of a public supply; and if I pass alternate currents originating in Deptford through this Ruhmkorff coil, which acts as what is now called a "high potential transformer", and allow sparks from the secondary to pass in an inverted test tube between platinum points, we shall be able to show in a comparatively short time a pretty rapid absorption of the gases. The electric current is led into the working chamber through bent glass tubes containing mercury, and provided at their inner extremities with platinum points. In this arrangement we avoid the risk, which would otherwise be serious, of a fracture just when we least desired it. I now start the sparks by switching on the Ruhmkorff to the alternate current supply; and, if you will take note of the level of the liquid representing the quantity of mixed gases included, I think you will see after, perhaps, a quarter of an hour that the liquid has very appreciably risen, owing to the union of the nitrogen and the oxygen gases under the influence of the electrical discharge, and subsequent absorption of the resulting compound by the alkaline liquid with which the gas space is enclosed.

By means of this little apparatus, which is very convenient for operations upon a moderate scale, such as analyses of "nitrogen" for the amount of argon that it may contain, we are able to get an absorption of about 80 cubic centimetres per hour, or about 4 inches along this test tube, when all is going well. In order, however, to effect the isolation of argon on any considerable scale by means of the oxygen method, we must employ an apparatus still more enlarged. The isolation of argon requires the removal of nitrogen, and, indeed, of very large quantities of nitrogen, for, as it appears, the proportion of argon contained in atmospheric nitrogen is only about 1 per cent., so that for every litre of argon that you wish to get you must eat up some hundred litres of nitrogen. That, however, can be done upon an adequate scale by calling to our aid the powerful electric discharge now obtainable by means of the alternate current supply and high potential transformers.

In what I have done upon this subject I have had the advantage of the advice of Mr Crookes, who some years ago drew special attention to the electric discharge or flame, and showed that many of its properties depended upon the fact that it had the power of causing, upon a very considerable scale, a combination of the nitrogen and the oxygen of the air in which it was made.

I had first thought of showing in the lecture room the actual apparatus which I have employed for the concentration of argon; but the difficulty is that, as the apparatus has to be used, the working parts are almost invisible, and I came to the conclusion that it would really be more instructive as well as more convenient to show the parts isolated, a very little effort of imagination being then all that is required in order to reconstruct in the mind the actual arrangements employed.

First, as to the electric arc or flame itself. We have here a transformer made by Pike and Harris. It is not the one that I have used in practice; but it is convenient for certain purposes, and it can be connected by means of a switch with the alternate currents of 100 volts furnished by the Supply Company. The platinum terminals that you see here are modelled exactly upon the plan of those which have been employed in practice. I may say a word or two on the question of mounting. The terminals require to be very massive on account of the heat evolved. In this case they consist of platinum wire doubled upon itself six times. The platinums are continued by iron wires going through glass tubes, and attached at the ends to the copper leads. For better security, the tubes themselves are stopped at the lower ends with corks and charged with water, the advantage being that, when the whole arrangement is fitted by means of an indiarubber stopper into a closed vessel, you have a witness that, as long as the water remains in position, no leak can have occurred through the insulating tubes conveying the electrodes.

Now, if we switch on the current and approximate the points sufficiently, we get the electric flame. There you have it. It is, at present, showing a certain amount of soda. That in time would burn off. After the arc has once been struck, the platinums can be separated; and then you have two tongues of fire ascending almost independently of one another, but meeting above. Under the influence of such a flame, the oxygen and the nitrogen of the air combine at a reasonable rate, and in this way the nitrogen is got rid of. It is now only a question of boxing up the gas in a closed space, where the argon concentrated by the combustion of the nitrogen can be collected. But there are difficulties to be encountered here. One cannot well use anything but a glass vessel. There is hardly any metal available that will withstand the action of strong caustic alkali and of the nitrous fumes resulting from the flame. One is practically limited to glass. The glass vessel employed is a large flask with a single neck, about half full of caustic alkali. The electrodes are carried through the neck by means of an indiarubber bung provided also with tubes for leading in the gas. The electric flame is situated at a distance of only about half an inch above the caustic alkali. In that way an efficient circulation is established; the hot gases as they rise from the flame strike the top, and then as they come round again in the course of the circulation they pass sufficiently close to the caustic alkali to ensure an adequate removal of the nitrous fumes.

There is another point to be mentioned. It is necessary to keep the vessel cool; otherwise the heat would soon rise to such a point that there would be excessive generation of steam, and then the operation would come to a standstill. In order to meet this difficulty the upper part of the vessel is provided with a water-jacket, in which a circulation can be established. No doubt the glass is severely treated, but it seems to stand it in a fairly amiable manner.

By means of an arrangement of this kind, taking nearly three horse-power from the electric supply, it is possible to consume nitrogen at a reasonable rate. The transformers actually used are the "Hedgehog" transformers of Mr Swinburne, intended to transform from 100 volts to 2400 volts. By Mr Swinburne's advice I have used two such, the fine wires being in series so as to accumulate the electrical potential and the thick wires in parallel. The rate at which the mixed gases are absorbed is about seven litres per hour; and the apparatus, when once fairly started, works very well as a rule, going for many hours without attention. At times the arc has a trick of going out, and it then requires to be restarted by approximating the platinums. We have already worked 14 hours on end, and by the aid of one or two automatic appliances it would, I think, be possible to continue operations day and night.

The gases, air and oxygen in about equal proportions, are mixed in a large gas-holder, and are fed automatically as required. The argon gradually accumulates; and when it is desired to stop operations the supply of nitrogen is cut off, and only pure oxygen allowed admittance. In this way the remaining nitrogen is consumed, so that, finally, the working vessel is charged with a mixture of argon and oxygen only, from which the oxygen is removed by ordinary well-known chemical methods. I may mention that at the close of the operation, when the nitrogen is all gone, the arc changes its appearance, and becomes of a brilliant blue colour.

I have said enough about this method, and I must now pass on to the alternative method which has been very successful in Professor Ramsay's hands—that of absorbing nitrogen by means of red-hot magnesium. By the kindness of Professor Ramsay and Mr Matthews, his assistant, we have here the full scale apparatus before us almost exactly as they use it. On the left there is a reservoir of nitrogen derived from air by the simple removal of oxygen. The gas is then dried. Here it is bubbled through sulphuric acid. It then passes through a long tube made of hard glass and charged with magnesium in the form of thin turnings. During the passage of the gas over the magnesium at a bright red heat, the nitrogen is absorbed in a great degree, and the gas which finally passes through is immensely richer in argon than that which first enters the hot tube. At the present time you see a tolerably rapid bubbling on the left, indicative of the flow of atmospheric nitrogen into the combustion furnace; whereas, on the right, the outflow is very much slower. Care must be taken to prevent the heat rising to such a point as to soften the glass. The concentrated argon is collected in a second gas-holder, and afterwards submitted to further treatment. The apparatus employed by Professor Ramsay in the subsequent treatment is exhibited in the diagram, and is very effective for its purpose; but I am afraid that the details of it would not readily be followed from any explanation that I could give in the time at my disposal. The principle consists in the circulation of the mixture of nitrogen and argon over hot magnesium, the gas being made to pass round and round until the nitrogen is effectively removed from it. At the end that operation, as in the case of the oxygen method, proceeds somewhat slowly. When the greater part of the nitrogen is gone, the remainder seems to be unwilling to follow, and it requires somewhat protracted treatment in order to be sure that the nitrogen has wholly disappeared. When I say "wholly disappeared", that, perhaps, would be too much to say in any case. What we can say is that the spectrum test is adequate to show the presence, or at any rate to show the addition, of about one-and-a-half per cent. of nitrogen to argon as pure as we can get it; so that it is fair to argue that any nitrogen at that stage remaining in the argon is only a small fraction of one-and-a-half per cent.

I should have liked at this point to be able to give advice as to which of the two methods—the oxygen method or the magnesium method—is the easier and the more to be recommended; but I confess that I am quite at a loss to do so. One difficulty in the comparison arises from the fact that they have been in different hands. As far as I can estimate, the quantities of nitrogen eaten up in a given time are not very different. In that respect, perhaps, the magnesium method has some advantage; but, on the other hand, it may be said that the magnesium process requires a much closer supervision, so that, perhaps, fourteen hours of the oxygen method may not unfairly compare with eight hours or so of the magnesium method. In practice a great deal would depend upon whether in any particular laboratory alternate currents are available from a public supply. If the alternate currents are at hand, I think it may probably be the case that the oxygen method is the easier; but, otherwise, the magnesium method would, probably, be preferred, especially by chemists who are familiar with operations conducted in red-hot tubes.

I have here another experiment illustrative of the reaction between magnesium and nitrogen. Two rods of that metal are suitably mounted in an atmosphere of nitrogen, so arranged that we can bring them into contact and cause an electric arc to form between them. Under the action of the heat of the electric arc the nitrogen will combine with the magnesium; and if we had time to carry out the experiment we could demonstrate a rapid absorption of nitrogen by this method. When the experiment was first tried, I had hoped that it might be possible, by the aid of electricity, to start the action so effectively that the magnesium would continue to burn independently under its own developed heat in the atmosphere of nitrogen. Possibly, on a larger scale, something of this sort might succeed, but I bring it forward here only as an illustration. We turn on the electric current, and bring the magnesiums together. You see a brilliant green light, indicating the vaporisation of the magnesium. Under the influence of the heat the magnesium burns, and there is collected in the glass vessel a certain amount of brownish-looking powder which consists mainly of the nitride of magnesium. Of course, if there is any oxygen present it has the preference, and the ordinary white oxide of magnesium is formed.

The gas thus isolated is proved to be inert by the very fact of its isolation. It refuses to combine under circumstances in which nitrogen, itself always considered very inert, does combine—both in the case of the oxygen treatment and in the case of the magnesium treatment; and these facts are, perhaps, almost enough to justify the name which we have suggested for it. But, in addition to this, it has been proved to be inert under a considerable variety of other conditions such as might have been expected to tempt it into combination. I will not recapitulate all the experiments which have been tried, almost entirely by Professor Ramsay, to induce the gas to combine. Hitherto, in our hands, it has not done so; and I may mention that recently, since the publication of the abstract of our paper read before the Royal Society, argon has been submitted to the action of titanium at a red heat, titanium being a metal having a great affinity for nitrogen, and that argon has resisted the temptation to which nitrogen succumbs. We never have asserted, and we do not now assert, that argon can under no circumstances be got to combine. That would, indeed, be a rash assertion for any one to venture upon; and only within the last few weeks there has been a most interesting announcement by M. Berthelot, of Paris, that, under the action of the silent electric discharge, argon can be absorbed when treated in contact with the vapour of benzine. Such a statement, coming from so great an authority, commands our attention; and if we accept the conclusion, as I suppose we must do, it will follow that argon has, under those circumstances, combined.

Argon is rather freely soluble in water. That is a thing that troubled us at first in trying to isolate the gas; because, when one was dealing with very small quantities, it seemed to be always disappearing. In trying to accumulate it we made no progress. After a sufficient quantity had been prepared, special experiments were made on the solubility of argon in water. It has been found that argon, prepared both by the magnesium method and by the oxygen method, has about the same solubility in water as oxygen some two-and-a-half times the solubility of nitrogen. This suggests, what has been verified by experiment, that the dissolved gases of water should contain a larger proportion of argon than does atmospheric nitrogen. I have here an apparatus of a somewhat rough description, which I have employed in experiments of this kind. The boiler employed consists of an old oil-can. The water is supplied to it and drawn from it by coaxial tubes of metal. The incoming cold water flows through the outer annulus between the two tubes. The outgoing hot water passes through the inner tube, which ends in the interior of the vessel at a higher level. By means of this arrangement the heat of the water which has done its work is passed on to the incoming water not yet in operation, and in that way a limited amount of heat is made to bring up to the boil a very much larger quantity of water than would otherwise be possible, the greater part of the dissolved gases being liberated at the same time. These are collected in the ordinary way. What you see in this flask is dissolved air collected out of water in the course of the last three or four hours. Such gas, when treated as if it were atmospheric nitrogen, that is to say after removal of the oxygen and minor impurities, is found to be decidedly heavier than atmospheric nitrogen to such an extent as to indicate that the proportion of argon contained is about double. It is obvious, therefore, that the dissolved gases of water form a convenient source of argon, by which some of the labour of separation from air is obviated. During the last few weeks I have been supplied from Manchester by Mr Macdougall, who has interested himself in this matter, with a quantity of dissolved gases obtained from the condensing water of his steam engine.

As to the spectrum, we have been indebted from the first to Mr Crookes, and he has been good enough to-night to bring some tubes which he will operate, and which will show you at all events the light of the electric discharge in argon. I cannot show you the spectrum of argon, for unfortunately the amount of light from a vacuum tube is not sufficient for the projection of its spectrum. Under some circumstances the light is red, and under other circumstances it is blue. Of course when these lights are examined with the spectroscope—and they have been examined by Mr Crookes with great care—the differences in the colour of the light translate themselves into different groups of spectrum lines. We have before us Mr Crookes' map, showing the two spectra upon a very large scale. The upper is the spectrum of the blue light; the lower is the spectrum of the red light; and it will be seen that they differ very greatly. Some lines are common to both; but a great many lines are seen only in the red, and others are seen only in the blue. It is astonishing to notice what trifling changes in the conditions of the discharge bring about such extensive alterations in the spectrum.

One question of great importance upon which the spectrum throws light is, Is the argon derived by the oxygen method really the same as the argon derived by the magnesium method? By Mr Crookes' kindness I have had an opportunity of examining the spectra of the two gases side by side, and such examination as I could make revealed no difference whatever in the two spectra, from which, I suppose, we may conclude either that the gases are absolutely the same, or, if they are not the same, that at any rate the ingredients by which they differ cannot be present in more than a small proportion in either of them.

My own observations upon the spectrum have been made principally at atmospheric pressure. In the ordinary process of sparking, the pressure is atmospheric; and, if we wish to look at the spectrum, we have nothing more to do than to include a jar in the circuit, and to put a direct-vision prism to the eye. At my request, Professor Schuster examined some tubes containing argon at atmospheric pressure prepared by the oxygen method, and I have here a diagram of a characteristic group. He also placed upon the sketch some of the lines of zinc, which were very convenient as directing one exactly where to look. See figure.

G

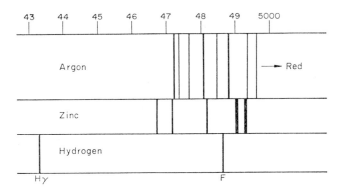

Within the last few days, Mr Crookes has charged a radiometer with argon. When held in the light from the electric lamp, the vanes revolve rapidly. Argon is anomalous in many respects, but not, you see, in this.

Next, as to the density of argon. Professor Ramsay has made numerous and careful observations upon the density of the gas prepared by the magnesium method, and he finds a density of about 19·9 as compared with hydrogen. Equally satisfactory observations upon the gas derived by the oxygen method have not yet been made*, but there is no reason to suppose that the density is different, such numbers as 19·7 having been obtained.

One of the most interesting matters in connection with argon, however, is what is known as the ratio of the specific heats. I must not stay to elaborate the questions involved, but it will be known to many who hear me that the velocity of sound in a gas depends upon the ratio of two specific heats—the specific heat of the gas measured at constant pressure, and the specific heat measured at constant volume. If we know the density of a gas, and also the velocity of sound in it, we are in a position to infer this ratio of specific heats; and by means of this method, Professor Ramsay has determined the ratio in the case of argon, arriving at the very

* [See *Proc. Roy. Soc.* Vol. LIX, p. 198, 1896.]

remarkable result that the ratio of specific heats is represented by the number 1·65, approaching very closely to the theoretical limit, 1·67. The number 1·67 would indicate that the gas has no energy except energy of translation of its molecules. If there is any other energy than that, it would show itself by this number dropping below 1·67. Ordinary gases, oxygen, nitrogen, hydrogen, &c., do drop below, giving the number 1·4. Other gases drop lower still. If the ratio of specific heats is 1·65, practically 1·67, we may infer that the whole energy of motion is translational; and from that it would seem to follow by arguments which, however, I must not stop to elaborate, that the gas must be of the kind called by chemists monatomic.

I had intended to say something of the operation of determining the ratio of specific heats, but time will not allow. The result is, no doubt, very awkward. Indeed, I have seen some indications that the anomalous properties of argon are brought as a kind of accusation against us. But we had the very best intentions in the matter. The facts were too much for us; and all that we can do now is to apologise for ourselves and for the gas.

Several questions may be asked, upon which I should like to say a word or two, if you will allow me to detain you a little longer. The first question (I do not know whether I need ask it) is, Have we got hold of a new gas at all? I had thought that that might be passed over, but only this morning I read in a technical journal the suggestion that argon was our old friend nitrous oxide. Nitrous oxide has roughly the density of argon; but that, so far as I can see, is the only point of resemblance between them.

Well, supposing that there is a new gas, which I will not stop to discuss, because I think that the spectrum alone would be enough to prove it, the next question that may be asked is, Is it in the atmosphere? This matter naturally engaged our earnest attention at an early stage of the enquiry. I will only indicate in a few words the arguments which seem to us to show that the answer must be in the affirmative.

In the first place, if argon be not in the atmosphere, the original discrepancy of densities which formed the starting-point of the

G*

investigation remains unexplained, and the discovery of the new gas has been made upon a false clue. Passing over that, we have the evidence from the blank experiments, in which nitrogen originally derived from chemical sources is treated either with oxygen or with magnesium, exactly as atmospheric nitrogen is treated. If we use atmospheric nitrogen, we get a certain propotion of argon, about 1 per cent. If we treat chemical nitrogen in the same way we get, I will not say absolutely nothing, but a mere fraction of what we should get had atmospheric nitrogen been the subject. You may ask, Why do we get any fraction at all from chemical nitrogen? It is not difficult to explain the small residue, because in the manipulation of the gases large quantities of water are used; and, as I have already explained, water dissolves argon somewhat freely. In the processes of manipulation some of the argon will come out of solution, and it remains after all the nitrogen has been consumed.

Another wholly distinct argument is founded upon the method of diffusion introduced by Graham. Graham showed that if you pass gas along porous tubes you alter the composition, if the gas is a mixture. The lighter constituents go more readily through the pores than do the heavier ones. The experiment takes this form. A number of tobacco pipes—eight in the actual arrangement— are joined together in series with indiarubber junctions, and they are put in a space in which a vacuum can be made, so that the space outside the porous pipes is vacuous or approximately so. Through the pipes ordinary air is led. One end may be regarded as open to the atmosphere. The other end is connected with an aspirator so arranged that the gas collected is only some 2 per cent. of that which leaks through the porosities. The case is like that of an Australian river drying up almost to nothing in the course of its flow. Well, if we treat air in that way, collecting only the small residue which is less willing than the remainder to penetrate the porous walls, and then prepare "nitrogen" from it by removal of oxygen and moisture, we obtain a gas heavier than atmospheric nitrogen, a result which proves that the ordinary nitrogen of the atmosphere is not a simple body, but is capable of being divided into parts by so simple an agent as the tobacco pipe.

If it be admitted that the gas is in the atmosphere, the further question arises as to its nature.

At this point I would wish to say a word of explanation. Neither in our original announcement at Oxford, nor at any time since, until the 31st of January, did we utter a word suggesting that argon was an element; and it was only after the experiments upon the specific heats that we thought that we had sufficient to go upon in order to make any such suggestion in public. I will not insist that that observation is absolutely conclusive. It is certainly strong evidence. But the subject is difficult, and one that has given rise to some difference of opinion among physicists. At any rate this property distinguishes argon very sharply from all the ordinary gases.

One question which occurred to us at the earliest stage of the enquiry, as soon as we knew that the density was not very different from 21, was the question of whether, possibly, argon could be a more condensed form of nitrogen, denoted chemically by the symbol N_3. There seem to be several difficulties in the way of this supposition. Would such a constitution be consistent with the ratio of specific heats (1·65)? That seems extremely doubtful. Another question is, Can the density be really as high as 21, the number required on the supposition of N_3? As to this matter, Professor Ramsay has repeated his measurements of density, and he finds that he cannot get even so high as 20. To suppose that the density of argon is really 21, and that it appears to be 20 in consequence of nitrogen still mixed with it, would be to suppose a contamination with nitrogen out of all proportion to what is probable. It would mean some 14 per cent. of nitrogen, whereas it seems that from one-and-a-half to two per cent. is easily enough detected by the spectroscope. Another question that may be asked is, Would N_3 require so much cooling to condense it as argon requires?

There is one other matter on which I would like to say a word— the question as to what N_3 would be like if we had it. There seems to be a great discrepancy of opinions. Some high authorities, among whom must be included, I see, the celebrated Mendeleef, consider that N_3 would be an exceptionally stable body; but most of the chemists with whom I have consulted are of opinion that N_3 would be explosive, or, at any rate, absolutely unstable. That is a question which may be left for the future to decide. We must not attempt to put these matters too positively. The balance of evidence still seems to be against the supposition that argon is N_3, but for my part I do not wish to dogmatise.

A few weeks ago we had an eloquent lecture from Professor Rücker on the life and work of the illustrious Helmholtz. It will be known to many that during the last few months of his life Helmholtz lay prostrate in a semi-paralysed condition, forgetful of many things, but still retaining a keen interest in science. Some little while after his death we had a letter from his widow, in which she described how interested he had been in our preliminary announcement at Oxford upon this subject, and how he desired the account of it to be read to him over again. He added the remark, "I always thought that there must be something more in the atmosphere."

On the Cooling of Air by Radiation and Conduction, and on the Propagation of Sound (1899)

[*Philosophical Magazine*, XLVII, pp. 308–314, 1899]

Editorial Preface

The modern acoustical interest in this paper is found in the final paragraph of the selection presented here. So far as is known this is the first suggestion of what has come to be known as a relaxation mechanism for the attenuation of sound in material media. This has served as the foundation of modern molecular acoustics, a large and growing area of research in sound propagation.

The balance of the paper (omitted here) is devoted more specifically to the radiating power of air, and though interesting, is not so relevant to modern research.

According to Laplace's theory of the propagation of Sound the expansions (and the contractions) of the air are supposed to take place without transfer of heat. Many years ago Sir G. Stokes* discussed the question of the influence of radiation from the heated air upon the propagation of sound. He showed that such small radiating power as is admissible would tell rather upon the intensity than upon the velocity. If x be measured in the direction of propagation, the factor expressing the diminution of amplitude is e^{-mx}, where

$$m = \frac{\gamma - 1}{\gamma} \frac{q}{2a}. \tag{1}$$

In (1) γ represents the ratio of specific heats (1·41), a is the velocity of sound, and q is such that e^{-qt} represents the law of cooling by radiation of a small mass of air maintained at constant

* *Phil. Mag.* [4] I, p. 305, 1851; *Theory of Sound*, § 247.

volume. If τ denote the time required to traverse the distance x, $\tau = x/a$, and (1) may be taken to assert that the amplitude falls to any fraction, *e.g.* one-half, of its original value in 7 times the interval of time required by a mass of air to cool to the same fraction of its original excess of temperature. "There appear to be no data by which the latter interval can be fixed with any approach to precision; but if we take it at one minute, the conclusion is that sound would be propagated for (seven) minutes, or travel over about (80) miles, without very serious loss from this cause*." We shall presently return to the consideration of the probable value of q.

Besides radiation there is also to be considered the influence of conductivity in causing transfer of heat, and further there are the effects of viscosity. The problems thus suggested have been solved by Stokes and Kirchhoff†. If the law of propagation be

$$u = e^{-m'x} \cos (nt - x/a), \qquad (2)$$

then
$$m' = \frac{n^2}{2a^3} \left\{ \tfrac{4}{3}\mu' + \nu \frac{\gamma - 1}{\gamma} \right\}, \qquad (3)$$

in which the frequency of vibration is $n/2\pi$, μ' is the kinematic viscosity, and ν the thermometric conductivity. In C.G.S. measure we may take $\mu' = \cdot14$, $\nu = \cdot26$, so that

$$\tfrac{4}{3}\mu' + \nu \frac{\gamma - 1}{\gamma} = \cdot25.$$

To take a particular case, let the frequency be 256; then since $a = 33200$, we find for the time of propagation during which the amplitude diminishes in the ratio of $e:1$,

$$(m'a)^{-1} = 3560 \text{ seconds.}$$

Accordingly it is only very high sounds whose propagation can be appreciably influenced by viscosity and conductivity.

* *Proc. Roy. Inst.* April 9, 1897. [Art. 228.]
† *Pogg. Ann.*, Vol. CXXXIV, p. 177, 1868; *Theory of Sound*, 2nd ed., § 348.

If we combine the effects of radiation with those of viscosity and conduction, we have as the factor of attenuation

$$e^{-(m+m')\ x},$$

where $$m + m' = \cdot14\,(q/a) + \cdot12\,(n^2/a^3).\qquad(4)$$

In actual observations of sound we must expect the intensity to fall off in accordance with the law of inverse squares of distances. A very little experience of moderately distant sounds shows that in fact the intensity is in a high degree uncertain. These discrepancies are attributable to atmospheric refraction and reflexion, and they are sometimes very surprising. But the question remains whether in a uniform condition of the atmosphere the attenuation is sensibly more rapid than can be accounted for by the law of inverse squares. Some interesting experiments towards the elucidation of this matter have been published by Mr Wilmer Duff*, who compared the distances of audibility of sounds proceeding respectively from two and from eight similar whistles. On an average the eight whistles were audible only about one-fourth further than a pair of whistles; whereas, if the sphericity of the waves had been the only cause of attenuation, the distances would have been as 2 to 1. Mr Duff considers that in the circumstances of his experiments there was little opportunity for atmospheric irregularities, and he attributes the greater part of the falling off to radiation. Calculating from (1) he deduces a radiating power such that a mass of air at any given excess of temperature above its surroundings will (if its volume remain constant) fall by radiation to one-half of that excess in about one-twelfth of a second.

In this paper I propose to discuss further the question of the radiating power of air, and I shall contend that on various grounds it is necessary to restrict it to a value hundreds of times smaller than that above mentioned. On this view Mr Duff's results remain unexplained. For myself I should still be disposed to attribute them to atmospheric refraction. If further experiment

* *Phys. Review*, Vol. VI, p. 129, 1898.

should establish a rate of attenuation of the order in question as applicable in uniform air, it will I think be necessary to look for a cause not hitherto taken into account. We might imagine a delay in the equalization of the different sorts of energy in a gas undergoing compression, not wholly insensible in comparison with the time of vibration of the sound. If in the dynamical theory we assimilate the molecules of a gas to hard smooth bodies which are nearly but not absolutely spherical, and trace the effect of a rapid compression, we see that at the first moment the increment of energy is wholly translational and thus produces a maximum effect in opposing the compression. A little later a due proportion of the excess of energy will have passed into rotational forms which do not influence the pressure, and this will accordingly fall off. Any effect of the kind must give rise to dissipation, and the amount of it will increase with the time required for the transformations, *i.e.* in the above mentioned illustration with the degree of approximation to the spherical form. In the case of absolute spheres no transformation of translatory into rotatory energy, or *vice versa*, would occur in a finite time. There appears to be nothing in the behaviour of gases, as revealed to us by experiment, which forbids the supposition of a delay capable of influencing the propagation of sound.

Remarks upon the
Law of Complete Radiation (1900)

[*Philosophical Magazine*, XLIX, pp. 539, 540, 1900]

Editorial Preface

In this paper Rayleigh derived in simple fashion the famous inverse fourth power law for the distribution of energy in the spectrum of black body radiation as a function of wavelength. This law, later known as the Rayleigh–Jeans law, fits the experimentally observed facts at the long wavelength end of the spectrum. It anticipated in time of publication by some six months the formula of Planck which fitted the whole spectrum and introduced the quantum concept into physics. It is interesting to note that in Planck's various papers from 1900 to 1910 on the radiation law he nowhere makes reference to this article by Rayleigh. It is true that in a paper on heat radiation written in 1910 Planck refers to the paper of Jeans of 1909 in which the latter essentially reproduced Rayleigh's result in a somewhat more elaborate manner. It was only in his paper at the first Solvay Conference in Brussels in 1911 that Planck referred to this 1900 paper of Rayleigh.

By complete radiation I mean the radiation from an ideally black body, which according to Stewart* and Kirchhoff is a definite function of the absolute temperature θ and the wavelength λ. Arguments of (in my opinion†) considerable weight have been brought forward by Boltzmann and W. Wien leading to the conclusion that the function is of the form

$$\theta^5 \, \phi \, (\theta\lambda) \, d\lambda, \tag{1}$$

expressive of the energy in that part of the spectrum which lies between λ and $\lambda + d\lambda$. A further specialization by determining the form of the function ϕ was attempted later‡. Wien concludes that the actual law is

* Stewart's work appears to be insufficiently recognized upon the Continent. [See *Phil. Mag.* I, p. 98, 1901.]

† *Phil. Mag.* Vol. XLV, p. 522 (1898). [Art. 238.]

‡ *Wied. Ann.* Vol. LVIII, p. 662 (1896).

$$c_1 \lambda^{-5} e^{-c_2/\lambda\theta}\, d\lambda, \qquad (2)$$

in which c_1 and c_2 are constants, but viewed from the theoretical side the result appears to me to be little more than a conjecture. It is, however, supported upon general thermodynamic grounds by Planck*.

Upon the experimental side, Wien's law (2) has met with important confirmation. Paschen finds that his observations are well represented if he takes

$$c_2 = 14{,}455,$$

θ being measured in centigrade degrees and λ in thousandths of a millimetre (μ). Nevertheless, the law seems rather difficult of acceptance, especially the implication that as the temperature is raised, the radiation of given wave-length approaches a limit. It is true that for visible rays the limit is out of range. But if we take $\lambda = 60\,\mu$, as (according to the remarkable researches of Rubens) for the rays selected by reflexion at surfaces of Sylvin, we see that for temperatures over $1000°$ (absolute) there would be but little further increase of radiation.

The question is one to be settled by experiment; but in the meantime I venture to suggest a modification of (2), which appears to me more probable *à priori*. Speculation upon this subject is hampered by the difficulties which attend the Boltzmann-Maxwell doctrine of the partition of energy. According to this doctrine every mode of vibration should be alike favoured; and although for some reason not yet explained the doctrine fails in general, it seems possible that it may apply to the graver modes. Let us consider in illustration the case of a stretched string vibrating transversely. According to the Boltzmann-Maxwell law the energy should be equally divided among all the modes, whose frequencies are as $1, 2, 3, \ldots$. Hence if k be the reciprocal of λ, representing the frequency, the energy between the limits k and $k + dk$ is (when k is large enough) represented by dk simply.

† *Wied. Ann.* Vol. I, p. 74 (1900).

When we pass from one dimension to three dimensions, and consider for example the vibrations of a cubical mass of air, we have (*Theory of Sound*, § 267) as the equation for k^2,

$$k^2 = p^2 + q^2 + r^2,$$

where p, q, r are integers representing the number of subdivisions in the three directions. If we regard p, q, r as the coordinates of points forming a cubic array, k is the distance of any point from the origin. Accordingly the number of points for which k lies between k and $k + dk$, proportional to the volume of the corresponding spherical shell, may be represented by k^2dk, and this expresses the distribution of energy according to the Boltzmann-Maxwell law, so far as regards the wave-length or frequency. If we apply this result to radiation, we shall have, since the energy in each mode is proportional to θ,

$$\theta k^2 dk, \tag{3}$$

or, if we prefer it,

$$\theta \lambda^{-4} d\lambda. \tag{4}$$

It may be regarded as some confirmation of the suitability of (4) that it is of the prescribed form (1).

The suggestion is that (4) rather than, as according to (2),

$$\lambda^{-5} d\lambda \tag{5}$$

may be the proper form when $\lambda\theta$ is great*. If we introduce the exponential factor, the complete expression will be

$$c_1 \theta \lambda^{-4} e^{-c_2/\lambda\theta} d\lambda. \tag{6}$$

If, as is probably to be preferred, we make k the independent variable, (6) becomes

$$c_1 \theta k^2 e^{-c_2 k/\theta} dk. \tag{7}$$

---

* [1902. This is what I intended to emphasize. Very shortly afterwards the anticipation above expressed was confirmed by the important researches of Rubens and Kurlbaum (*Drude Ann.* IV, p. 649, 1901), who operated with exceptionally long waves. The formula of Planck, given about the same time, seems best to meet the observations. According to this modification of Wien's formula, $e^{-c_2/\lambda\theta}$ in (2) is replaced by $1 \div (e^{c_2/\lambda\theta} - 1)$. When $\lambda\theta$ is great, this becomes $\lambda\theta/c_2$ and the complete expression reduces to (4).]

Whether (6) represents the facts of observation as well as (2) I am not in a position to say. It is to be hoped that the question may soon receive an answer at the hands of the distinguished experimenters who have been occupied with this subject.

Is Rotatory Polarization influenced by the Earth's Motion? (1902)

[*Philosophical Magazine*, IV, pp. 215–220, 1902]

Editorial Preface

This paper is inserted here for two reasons. In the first place it illustrates Rayleigh's interest in the controversies excited over the problem of the nature of what was called in the late nineteenth century the lumeniferous aether, which of course led to the development of the special theory of relativity. In the second place the paper is another good example of Rayleigh's zeal for precise experimental work and his ability to get remarkably good results from relatively simple equipment. The paper proved to be another nail in the coffin of the aether.

The question whether the rotation of the plane of polarization of light propagated along the axis of a quartz crystal is affected by the direction of this axis relatively to that of the earth's orbital motion, is of considerable theoretical importance. According to an investigation of Lorentz, an effect of the first order might be looked for. Such an effect would be rendered apparent by comparing the rotations when the direction of propagation of the light is parallel to that of the earth's motion and in the reverse direction, and it might amount to $\frac{1}{10,000}$ of the whole rotation*. According to Larmor's theory† there should be no effect of the first order.

The question was examined experimentally many years ago by Mascart‡, who came to the conclusion that the reversal of the ray left the rotation unchanged to $\frac{1}{20,000}$ part. In most of the

* This fraction representing approximately the ratio of the velocity of the earth in its orbit to the velocity of light.
† *Æther and Matter*, Cambridge, 1900.
‡ *Annales de l'École Normale*, Vol. I, p. 157 (1872).

experiments, however, the accuracy was insufficient to lend support to the above conclusion.

Dr Larmor (*l. c.* p. 220) having expressed the opinion that it might be desirable to re-examine the question, I have made some observations which carry the test as far as can readily be done. It appears that the rotation is certainly not altered by $\frac{1}{100,000}$ part, and probably not by the half of this, when the direction of propagation of the light is altered from that of the earth's motion to the opposite direction.

I should scarcely have been able to carry the test to so satisfactory a point, had it not been for the kindness of Prof. MacGregor, who allowed me the use of certain valuable quartz crystals belonging to the Edinburgh collection of apparatus. These crystals, five in number, are all right-handed, and measure about 50 mm. each in the direction of the optical axis, to which the polished faces are approximately perpendicular. They were prepared for Prof. Tait, and were employed by him for his "rotatory polarization spectroscope of great dispersion*." For the most part they are nearly free from blemish, and well adapted to the purpose in view.

In principle the experiment is very simple, scarcely differing from ordinary polarimetry, as, for example, in determining the rotation due to sugar and other active bodies. But the apparatus needs to be specially mounted upon a long stiff board, itself supported upon a point, so that the absolute direction of the light may be reversed without danger of even the slightest relative displacement of the parts. The board swings round in the horizontal plane; and if its length is directed from east to west, or from west to east, observations taken at noon (in June) correspond pretty accurately to propagation of the light with or against the earth's motion in its orbit. Similar comparisons at 6 o'clock are nearly independent of the earth's motion.

In another respect the experiment is peculiar on account of the enormous amount of the rotation to be dealt with. For sodium light the rotation is 22° per millimetre of quartz, so that the whole

* *Nature*, Vol. XXII, 1880; Tait's *Scientific Papers*, Vol. I, p. 423.

rotation is 5500°, or more than 15 complete revolutions. In the preliminary experiments, with one of the crystals only, sodium light was employed; but the observations were unsatisfactory, even although the light was resolved into a spectrum. If the flame was well supplied with salt, the extinction of the D-line by suitable adjustment of the nicol still left the *neighbouring* region of the spectrum so bright as to prejudice the observation by lessening the sensitiveness of the eye. This effect, which is quite distinct from what is ordinarily called the broadening of the D-lines and can be made still more pronounced by stimulating the flame with oxygen, does not appear to present itself in any other method of observation, and is of interest in connexion with the theory of luminous emission. A very moderate rotation of the nicol revives the D-lines sufficiently to extinguish the neighbouring spectrum, just as the first glimpse of the limb of the sun after a total eclipse extinguishes the corona*.

When all five quartzes were brought into use it was hopeless to expect good results from a soda-flame. From the fact that the rotation is as λ^{-2} we see that there must be 11° difference of rotation for the two D-lines, so that a satisfactory extinction is out of the question. For the observations about to be recorded a so-called vacuum-tube, charged with *helium*, was employed, the yellow line (situated close to the D-lines) being chosen. It was actuated by a Ruhmkorff coil and four Grove cells, situated at some distance away.

The various parts, all mounted upon the pivoted board, will now be specified in order. First came the helium tube with capillary vertical, then at a distance of 25 cm. a collimating spectacle-lens, followed by the polarizing nicol. The field of view presented by this nicol was contracted to a circular aperture 7 mm. in diameter,

---

* *July* 6.—A doubt having suggested itself as to whether this effect might not be due to an actual whitening of the Bunsen flame, such as sometimes occurs rather unexpectedly, the experiment was repeated with a flame of pure *hydrogen*. The region of the spectrum in the neighbourhood of D was even brighter than before. An attempt to produce an analogous effect with *lithium* was a failure, apparently in consequence of insufficient brightness of the flame.

and was further divided into two parts by a "sugar-cell." This cell was the same as that formerly used in a cognate research on the rotation of the plane of polarization in bisulphide of carbon under magnetic force*. "The polarimeter employed is on the principle of Laurent, but according to a suggestion of Poynting (*Phil. Mag.* July 1880) the half-wave plate of quartz is replaced by a cell containing syrup, so arranged that the two halves of the field of view are subjected to small rotations differing by about 2°. The difference of thickness necessary is best obtained by introducing into the cell a piece of thick glass, the upper edge of which divides the field into two parts. The upper half of the field is then rotated by a thickness of syrup equal to the entire width of the cell (say $\frac{1}{2}$ inch), but in the lower half of the field part of the thickness of syrup is replaced by glass, and the rotation is correspondingly less. With a pretty strong syrup a difference of 2° may be obtained with a glass $\frac{3}{16}$ inch [inch = 2·54 cm.] thick. For the best results the operating boundary should be a true plane perpendicular to the face. The pieces used by me, however, were not worked, being simply cut with a diamond from thick plate glass; and there was usually no difficulty in finding a part of the edge sufficiently flat for the purpose, *i.e.* capable of exhibiting a field of view sharply divided into two parts . . . . By this use of sugar, half-shade polarimeters may be made of large dimensions at short notice and at very little cost. The syrup should be filtered (hot) through paper, and the cell must be closed to prevent evaporation."

The light next traversed the quartz crystals, each mounted upon a small stand admitting of adjustment in azimuth and level so as to bring the optical axis into parallelism with the line of vision. The analysing nicol, mounted near the end of the board, was distant 102 cm. from the polarizer. After passing the nicol the light traversed in succession a direct-vision prism of sufficient aperture and a small opera-glass focussed upon the sugar-cell. The aperture limiting the field had been so chosen that, as seen through the spectroscope, the yellow image under observation was sufficiently

* *Phil. Trans.* CLXXVI, p. 343 (1885). [Art. 118.]

separated from the neighbouring red and green images corresponding to other spectral lines of helium. The position of the analysing nicol was read with a vernier to tenths of a degree—an accuracy which just sufficed, and the setting could be made by causing the two halves of the field of view afforded by the sugar-cell to appear *equally* dark.

A good deal of time was spent in preliminary experiment before the best procedure was hit upon. It is necessary that the optic axes of the crystals be adjusted pretty accurately to the line of vision, and this in several cases involved considerable obliquity of the terminal faces. In these adjustments the sugar-cell and its diaphragm are best dispensed with, the crystals being turned until the rotation required to darken the field is a minimum and the darkness itself satisfactory. When the first crystal has been adjusted, a second is introduced and adjusted in its turn, and so on. In some cases a further shift of the crystal parallel to itself was required in order to remove an imperfection from the part of the field to be utilized. In the end a fairly satisfactory darkness was attained, but decidedly inferior to that obtainable when the quartzes were removed. Part of the residual light may have been due to want of adjustment; but more seemed to originate in imperfections in the quartzes themselves.

In my former experiments upon bisulphide of carbon advantage was found from a device for rocking the plane of polarization through a small constant angle*. During the observations now under discussion this effect was obtained by the introduction of a second sugar-cell, not divided into two parts or seen in focus, just in front of the analysing nicol. The cell was mounted so that it could slide horizontally in and out up to fixed stops. The thickness of the cell being sufficient, the strength of the syrup was adjusted to the desired point. Thus when the nicol was correctly set, the upper half of the field was *just distinctly* the brighter when the cell was *in*, and the lower half with *equal distinctness* the brighter when the cell was *out*, the object to be aimed at in the

* *Loc. cit.* [Art. 118.]

setting of the nicol being the *equality* of these small *differences*. For the results now to be given the setting of the nicol was by myself and the reading of the vernier was by Mr Gordon. A second observer is a distinct advantage.

As a specimen, chosen at random, I will give in full all the readings made in the neighbourhood of noon on June 19. Five readings were taken in each position and then the board was reversed. The headings "East" and "West" indicate the end at which the observer was sitting; "East" therefore meaning that the course of the light was from West to East.

The mean of the three "Easts" is 45·75, and of the two "Wests" is 45·71; so that

$$E - W = + \cdot 04°.$$

All these numbers are in decimals of a degree. The progressive alteration in the readings corresponds to the rise of temperature. It would appear that, as was natural, the quartzes lagged somewhat behind the thermometer.

TABLE I

Time 11ʰ 30ᵐ Temp. 17°·4 East	Time 11ʰ 50ᵐ Temp. 17°·7 West	Time 12ʰ 5ᵐ Temp. 17°·9 East	Time 12ʰ 15ᵐ Temp. 17°·9 West	Time 12ʰ 25ᵐ Temp. 17°·9 East
°	°	°	°	°
45·7	45·4	45·6	45·9	46·0
45·5	45·9	45·8	45·7	46·1
45·5	45·4	45·5	45·9	46·1
45·6	45·7	45·6	45·7	46·0
45·6	45·7	45·7	45·8	46·0
45·58	45·62	45·64	45·80	46·04

Three sets of observations were taken at noon, and the results are recorded in Table II. In two others sets taken about 6ʰ the differences $E - W$ were even less. The comparison of the two hours serves to check possible errors, *e.g.* of a magnetic character, such as might be caused by the magnetism of the Ruhmkorff coil, if insufficiently distant.

It seems certain that at neither hour does the difference $E - W$ actually amount to $\frac{1}{20}$ of a degree, *i.e.* to $\frac{1}{100,000}$ of the whole rotation. In all probability the influence of the reversal is much less, if indeed it exists at all.

TABLE II. Noon

Date	E.–W.
	$^{\circ}$
June 17	$+\cdot03$
,, 18	$-\cdot05$
,, 19	$+\cdot04$
Mean	$+\cdot007$

P.S. Since the above observations were made, I see from the *Amsterdam Proceedings* (May 28, 1902) that Lorentz maintains his opinion against the criticism of Larmor. Lorentz's theoretical result contains an unknown quantity which might be adjusted so as to make the influence of the earth's motion evanescent; but for this special adjustment there appears to be no theoretical reason. I hope that the above experimental demonstration of the absence of effect, to a high order of accuracy, will be found all the more interesting.

On Electrical Vibrations
and the Constitution of the Atom (1906)

[*Philosophical Magazine*, Vol. XI, pp. 117–123, 1906]

Editorial Preface

In this article, which is here reprinted in its entirety, Rayleigh shows his interest in early twentieth century efforts to develop a theory of atomic structure which would provide stability in the light of classical electromagnetic theory and at the same time account for the frequencies of the spectral lines emitted by the atom. He confesses himself baffled by the lack of success of attempts to solve this problem along classical lines and hints at the necessity for a more radical approach which, however, he himself does not seem prepared to embark on. The very last sentence is very suggestive in the light of the theory of Niels Bohr some half dozen years later.

In illustration of the view, suggested by Lord Kelvin, that an atom may be represented by a number of negative electrons, or negatively charged corpuscles, enclosed in a sphere of uniform positive electrification, Prof. J. J. Thomson has given some valuable calculations* of the stability of a ring of such electrons, uniformly spaced, and either at rest or revolving about a central axis. The corpuscles are supposed to repel one another according to the law of inverse square of distance and to be endowed with inertia, which may, however, be the inertia of æther in the immediate neighbourhood of each corpuscle. The effect of the sphere of positive electrification is merely to produce a field of force directly as the distance from the centre of the sphere. The artificiality of this hypothesis is partly justified by the necessity, in order to meet the facts, of introducing from the beginning some essential difference, other than of mere sign, between positive and negative.

* *Phil. Mag.* Vol. VII, p. 237 (1904).

Some of the most interesting of Prof. Thomson's results depend essentially upon the finiteness of the number of electrons; but since the experimental evidence requires that in any case the number should be very large, I have thought it worth while to consider what becomes of the theory when the number is infinite. The cloud of electrons may then be assimilated to a fluid whose properties, however, must differ in many respects from those with which we are most familiar. We suppose that the whole quantities of positive and negative are equal. The difference between them is that the positive is constrained to remain undisplaced, while the negative is free to move. In equilibrium the negative distributes itself with uniformity throughout the sphere occupied by the positive, so that the total density is everywhere zero. There is then no force at any point; but if the negative be displaced, a force is usually called into existence. We may denote the density of the negative at any time and place by ρ, that of the positive and of the negative, when in equilibrium, being ρ_0. The repulsion between two elements of negative ρdV, $\rho'dV'$ at distance r is denoted by

$$\gamma \cdot r^{-2} \cdot \rho dV \cdot \rho'dV'. \tag{1}$$

The negative fluid is supposed to move without circulation, so that a velocity-potential (ϕ) exists; and the first question which presents itself, is as to whether there is "condensation." If this be denoted by s, the equation of continuity is, as usual*,

$$\frac{ds}{dt} + \nabla^2\phi = 0. \tag{2}$$

Again, since there is no outstanding *pressure* to be taken into account, the dynamical equation assumes the form

$$\frac{d\phi}{dt} = R, \tag{3}$$

* *Theory of Sound*, § 244.

where R is the potential of the attractive and repulsive forces. Eliminating ϕ, we get

$$\frac{d^2s}{dt^2} = -\nabla^2 R. \tag{4}$$

In equilibrium R is zero, and the actual value depends upon the displacements, which are supposed to be small. By Poisson's formula

$$\nabla^2 R = 4\pi\gamma\rho_0 s, \tag{5}$$

so that

$$\frac{d^2s}{dt^2} + 4\pi\gamma\rho_0 s = 0. \tag{6}$$

This applies to the interior of the sphere; and it appears that any departure from a uniform distribution brings into play forces giving stability, and further that the times of oscillation are the same whatever be the character of the disturbance. It is worthy of note that the constant $(\gamma\rho_0)$ of itself determines a *time*.

In considering the significance of the vibrations expressed by (6), we must remember that when s is uniform no external forces having a potential are capable of disturbing the uniformity.

We now pass on to vibrations not involving a variable s, that is of such a kind that the fluid behaves as if incompressible. An irrotational displacement now requires that some of the negative fluid should traverse the surface of the positive sphere (a). In the interior $\nabla^2 R = 0$.

To represent simple vibrations we suppose that ϕ, &c. are proportional to e^{ipt}. By (3) $\nabla^2\phi = 0$; and we take (at any rate for trial)

$$\phi = e^{ipt}r^n S_n, \tag{7}$$

where S_n is a spherical surface harmonic of the nth order. The velocity across the surface of the sphere at $r = a$ is

$$d\phi/dr = na^{n-1}e^{ipt}S_n;$$

and thus the quantity of fluid which has passed the element of area $d\sigma$ at time t is

$$\rho\int\frac{d\phi}{dr}\,dt\,.\,d\sigma = \frac{\rho_0 na^{n-1}}{ip}\,e^{ipt}S_n d\sigma. \tag{8}$$

The next step is to form the expression for R, the potential of all the forces. In equilibrium the positive and negative densities everywhere neutralize one another, and thus in the displaced condition R may be regarded as due to the surface distribution (8). By a well-known theorem in Attractions we have

$$R = - \frac{4\pi\gamma\rho_0 n r^n S_n e^{ipt}}{ip(2n+1)}. \tag{9}$$

But by (3) this is equal to $d\phi/dt$, or $ipe^{ipt}r^n S_n$. The recovery of $r^n S_n$ proves that the form assumed is correct; and we find further that

$$p^2 = \frac{4\pi\gamma\rho_0 . n}{2n+1}. \tag{10}$$

This formula for the frequencies of vibration gives rise to two remarks. The frequency depends upon the density ρ_0, but not upon the radius (a) of the sphere. Again, as n increases, the pitch rises indeed, but approaches a finite limit given by $p^2 = 2\pi\gamma\rho_0$. The approach to a finite limit as we advance along the series is characteristic of the series of spectrum-lines found for hydrogen and the alkali metals, but in other respects the analogy fails. It is p^2, rather than p, which is simply expressed; and if we ignore this consideration and take the square root, supposing n large, we find

$$p \propto 1 - 1/2n,$$

whereas according to observation n^2 should replace n. Further, it is to be remarked that we have found only one series of frequencies. The different kinds of harmonics which are all of one order n do not give rise to different frequencies. Probably the simplicity of this result would be departed from if the number of electrons was treated merely as great but not infinite.

The principles which have led us to (10) seem to have affinity rather with the older views as to the behaviour of electricity upon a conductor than with those which we associate with the name of Maxwell. It is true that the vibrations above considered would be subject to dissipation in consequence of radiation, and that this dissipation would be very rapid, at any rate in the case of n equal to unity*. But this hardly explains the difference between the two views.

[1911. Some paragraphs dealing with the question of electrical vibrations outside a conducting sphere (J. J. Thomson, *Proc. Lond. Math. Soc.* Vol. xv. p. 197, 1884; *Recent Researches*, § 312, 1893), or of sonorous vibrations outside a rigid and fixed sphere, are omitted as involving a misconception. The matter had already been satisfactorily treated by Lamb (*Proc. Lond. Math. Soc.* Vol. XXXII. p. 208, 1900) and by Love (*Ibid.* Vol. II. p. 88, 1904).]

In the calculation of frequencies given above for a cloud of electrons the undisturbed condition is one of equilibrium, and the frequencies of radiation are those of vibration about this condition of equilibrium. Almost every theory of this kind is open to the objection that I put forward some years ago†, viz. that p^2, and not p, is given in the first instance. It is difficult to explain on this basis the simple expressions found for p, and the constant differences manifested in the formulae of Rydberg and of Kayser and Runge. There are, of course, particular cases where the square root can be taken without complication, and Ritz‡ has derived a differential equation leading to a formula of this description and capable of being identified with that of Rydberg. Apart from the question whether it corresponds with anything mechanically possible, this theory has too artificial an appearance to inspire much confidence.

A partial escape from these difficulties might be found in regarding actual spectrum lines as due to *difference tones* arising from primaries of much higher pitch,—a suggestion already put forward in a somewhat different form by Julius.

In recent years theories of atomic structure have found favour in which the electrons are regarded as describing orbits, probably with great rapidity. If the electrons are sufficiently numerous, there may be an approach to steady motion. In case of disturbance,

---

* In this case we should have to consider how the positive sphere is to be held at rest.

† *Phil. Mag.* XLIV, p. 362, 1897. [Art. 235.]

‡ Drude, *Ann.* Bd. XII, p. 264, 1903.

oscillations about this steady motion may ensue and these oscillations are regarded as the origin of luminous waves of the same frequency. But in view of the discrete character of electrons such a motion can never be fully steady, and the system must tend to radiate even when undisturbed*. In particular cases, such as some considered by Prof. Thomson, the radiation in the undisturbed state may be very feeble. After disturbance oscillations about the normal motion will ensue, but it does not follow that the frequencies of these oscillations will be manifested in the spectrum of the radiation. The spectrum may rather be due to the upsetting of the balance by which before disturbance radiation was prevented, and the frequencies will correspond (with modification) rather to the original distribution of electrons than to the oscillations. For example, if four equally spaced electrons revolve in a ring, the radiation is feeble and its frequency is four times that of revolution. If the disposition of equal spacing be disturbed, there must be a tendency to recovery and to oscillations about this disposition. These oscillations may be extremely slow; but nevertheless frequencies will enter into the radiation once, twice, and thrice as great as that of revolution, and with intensities which may be much greater than the original radiation of fourfold frequency.

An apparently formidable difficulty, emphasised by Jeans, stands in the way of all theories of this character. How can the atom have the definiteness which the spectroscope demands? It would seem that variations must exist in (say) hydrogen atoms which would be fatal to the sharpness of the observed radiation; and indeed the gradual change of an atom is directly contemplated in view of the phenomena of radioactivity. It seems an absolute necessity that the large majority of hydrogen atoms should be alike in a very high degree. Either the number undergoing change must be very small or else the changes must be sudden, so that at any time only a few deviate from one or more definite conditions.

It is possible, however, that the conditions of stability or of exemption from radiation may after all really demand this

* Confer Larmor, *Matter and Æther*.

definiteness, notwithstanding that in the comparatively simple cases treated by Thomson the angular velocity is open to variation. According to this view the frequencies observed in the spectrum may not be frequencies of disturbance or of oscillations in the ordinary sense at all, but rather form an essential part of the original constitution of the atom as determined by conditions of stability.

Note as to the Application of the Principle of Dynamical Similarity (1909-10)

[*Report of the Advisory Committee for Aeronautics*, 1909–10, p. 38]

Editorial Preface

This paper reflects Rayleigh's interest in problems in aerodynamics which were beginning to become important in his later years because of the rise of the aircraft industry. Here he discusses the problem of lift and drag on a simple airfoil moving relatively to a fluid medium and employs the method of dynamical similarity with some success.

Mr Lanchester has discussed the application of the principle of dynamical similarity to the problem of the resistances experienced by a plane plate immersed in a stream of fluid. A year or two ago I communicated to Dr Stanton a somewhat more general statement which may be found to possess advantages. We will commence by supposing the plane of the plate perpendicular to the stream and inquire as to the dependence of the forces upon the linear dimension (l) of the plate and upon the density (ρ), velocity (v), and kinematic viscosity (ν) of the fluid. Geometrical similarity is presupposed, and until the necessity is disproved it must be assumed to extend to the thickness of the plate as well as to the irregularities of surface which constitute roughness.

If the above-mentioned quantities suffice to determine the effects, the expression for the mean force per unit area normal to the plate (P), analogous to a pressure, is

$$P = \rho v^2 f.(\nu/vl), \qquad (A)$$

where f is an arbitrary function of the *one* variable ν/vl.

It is for experiment to determine the form of this function, or in the alternative to show that the facts cannot be represented at all by an equation of form (A). It is known that somewhat approximately P is proportional to v^2, and again that it is independent of l. If either of these approximations is supposed to hold good absolutely, it follows that f is constant, in which case P is independent of v, or conversely if P be independent of v, f must be constant.

The form of f may be determined by experiments in which v is varied while l and v are constant, or again by varying l while v and v are constant. A third method, not, it would seem, hitherto applied, is to vary v keeping l and v constant, and it would have certain advantages, especially in small scale experiments. The viscosity of water may be diminished (to about $\frac{1}{4}$) by heating it, or increased by admixture of alcohol.

The results of observations are best exhibited in the form of a curve, where the abscissa represents v/lv and the ordinate $P/\rho v^2$. An example of this method will be found in *Phil Mag.* Vol. XLVIII, p. 321, 1899, or *Scientific Papers*, [Art. 251] the subject being the size of drops formed under various conditions.

Similar principles apply when the direction of the stream is no longer perpendicular to the plate. Here of course we must have regard to the manner of presentation. Thus, if a rectangular plate is held at obliquity θ, we may suppose that the longer sides are always perpendicular to the current. Equation (A) still applies; only f must be regarded as a function also of θ. We may write

$$P = \rho v^2 . f(\theta, v/vl), \tag{B}$$

where there are now two independent variables. In the case of symmetrical shapes it is evident that f must be an *even* function of θ.

The expression for the mean *tangential* force, reckoned per unit of area, may be written in the same way. For symmetrical shapes

$$T = \rho v^2 . F(\theta, v/vl), \tag{C}$$

where F is now an odd function of θ, vanishing also with v. If $\theta = \frac{1}{2}\pi$, the plate is parallel to the stream, and the case is one previously considered (*Phil. Mag.* May 1904, p. 66*).

* [Art. 297.]

In (B) and (C) the forces are respectively normal and tangential to the plate. The components in other directions may at once be deduced. Thus the component in the direction of the stream is

$$P \cos \theta + T \sin \theta;$$

and it may be expressed in the form (B)

$$\rho v^2 . f_1(\theta, v/vl), \tag{D}$$

where f_1 is an even function of θ. When $\theta = 0$, f and f_1 coincide.

Letter to Professor Nernst (1911)

[*Conseil scientifique sous les auspices de M. Ernest Solvay*, Oct. 1911]

Editorial Preface

Rayleigh was invited to attend the first Solvay Conference in Brussels organized to discuss problems of the quantum theory, but found himself unable to go. This letter to Professor Walther Nernst on this occasion indicates Rayleigh's keen awareness of the difficulties involved in the classical molecular theory principle of equipartition of energy as well as his reluctance to accept the solution proposed by Planck and quantum theory adherents. The problem he posed about the vibrational specific heats of diatomic gases is now generally admitted to have been solved by the use of quantum statistics.

DEAR PROF. NERNST,

Having been honoured with an invitation to attend the Conference at Brussels, I feel that the least that I can do is to communicate my views, though I am afraid I can add but little to what has been already said upon the subject.

I wish to emphasize the difficulty mentioned in my paper of 1900* with respect to the use of generalized coordinates. The possibility of representing the state of a body by a finite number of such (short at any rate of the whole number of molecules) depends upon the assumption that a body may be treated as rigid, or incompressible, or in some other way simplified. The justification, and in many cases the sufficient justification, is that a departure from the simplified condition would involve such large amounts of potential energy as could not occur under the operation of the forces concerned. But the law of equipartition lays it down that every mode is to have its share of kinetic energy. If we begin by supposing an elastic body to be rather stiff, the vibrations have their full share and this share

* *Phil. Mag.* Vol. XLIX, p. 118. [Art. 253.]

216

cannot be diminished by increasing the stiffness. *For this purpose* the simplification fails, which is as much as to say that the method of generalized coordinates cannot be applied. The argument becomes, in fact, self-contradictory.

Perhaps this failure might be invoked in support of the views of Planck and his school that the laws of dynamics (as hitherto understood) cannot be applied to the smallest parts of bodies. But I must confess that I do not like this solution of the puzzle. Of course I have nothing to say against following out the consequences of the [quantum] theory of energy—a procedure which has already in the hands of able men led to some interesting conclusions. But I have a difficulty in accepting it as a picture of what actually takes place.

We do well, I think, to concentrate attention upon the diatomic gaseous molecule. Under the influence of collisions the molecule freely and rapidly acquires rotation. Why does it not also acquire vibration along the line joining the two atoms? If I rightly understand, the answer of Planck is that in consideration of the stiffness of the union the amount of energy that should be acquired at each collision falls below the minimum possible and that therefore none at all is acquired—an argument which certainly sounds paradoxical. On the other hand Boltzmann and Jeans contend that it is all a question of time and that the vibrations necessary for full statistical equilibrium may be obtained only after thousands of years. The calculations of Jeans appear to show that there is nothing forced in such a view. I should like to inquire is there any definite experimental evidence against it? So far as I know, ordinary laboratory experience affords nothing decisive.

I am yours truly,
RAYLEIGH.

The Pressure of
Radiation and Carnot's Principle (1914)

[*Nature*, Vol. XCII, pp. 527, 528, 1914]

Editorial Preface

This brief paper reflects Rayleigh's continued interest in the problem of radiation pressure, to which he had already paid considerable attention earlier for the case of mechanical radiation. In this paper he is concerned with electromagnetic radiation, and shows that the existence of radiation pressure in this case can be theoretically predicted by the use of the second law of thermodynamics.

As is well known, the pressure of radiation, predicted by Maxwell, and since experimentally confirmed by Lebedew and by Nichols and Hull, plays an important part in the theory of radiation developed by Boltzmann and W. Wien. The existence of the pressure according to electromagnetic theory is easily demonstrated*, but it does not appear to be generally remembered that it could have been deduced with some confidence from thermodynamical principles, even earlier than in the time of Maxwell. Such a deduction was, in fact, made by Bartoli in 1876, and constituted the foundation of Boltzmann's work†. Bartoli's method is quite sufficient for his purpose; but, mainly because it employs irreversible operations, it does not lend itself to further developments. It may therefore be of service to detail the elementary argument on the lines of Carnot, by which it appears

---

* See, for example, J. J. Thomson, *Elements of Electricity and Magnetism* (Cambridge, 1895, § 241); Rayleigh, *Phil. Mag.* Vol. XLV, p. 522 (1898). [Art. 238.]

† *Wied. Ann.* Vol. XXXII, pp. 31, 291 (1884). It is only through Boltzmann that I am acquainted with Bartoli's reasoning.

that in the absence of a pressure of radiation it would be possible to raise heat from a lower to a higher temperature.

The imaginary apparatus is, as in Boltzmann's theory, a cylinder and piston formed of perfectly reflecting material, within which we may suppose the radiation to be confined. This radiation is always of the kind characterised as complete (or black), a requirement satisfied if we include also a very small black body with which the radiation is in equilibrium. If the operations are slow enough, the size of the black body may be reduced without limit, and then the whole energy at a given temperature is that of the radiation and proportional to the volume occupied. When we have occasion to introduce or abstract heat, the communication may be supposed in the first instance to be with the black body. The operations are of two kinds: (1) compression (or rarefaction) of the kind called *adiabatic*, that is, without communication of heat. If the volume increases, the temperature must fall, even though in the absence of pressure upon the piston no work is done, since the same energy of complete radiation now occupies a larger space. Similarly a rise of temperature accompanies adiabatic contraction. In the second kind of operation (2) the expansions and contractions are *isothermal*—that is, without change of temperature. In this case heat must pass, into the black body when the volume expands and out of it when the volume contracts, and at a given temperature the amount of heat which must pass is proportional to the change of volume.

The cycle of operations to be considered is the same as in Carnot's theory, the only difference being that here, in the absence of pressure, there is no question of external work. Begin by isothermal expansion at the lower temperature during which heat is taken in. Then compress adiabatically until a higher temperature is reached. Next continue the compression isothermally until the same amount of heat is given out as was taken in during the first expansion. Lastly, restore the original volume adiabatically. Since no heat has passed upon the whole in either direction, the final state is identical with the initial state, the temperature being recovered as well as the volume. The sole result of the cycle is that heat is raised from a lower to a higher temperature. Since this is assumed to be impossible, the supposition that the operations can be performed without external work is to be rejected—in other words, we must regard the radiation as exercising a pressure upon the moving piston. Carnot's principle and the absence of a pressure are incompatible.

For a further discussion it is, of course, desirable to employ the general formulation of Carnot's principle, as in a former paper*. If p be the pressure, θ the absolute temperature,

$$\theta \frac{dp}{d\theta} = M, \tag{29}$$

where $M\,dv$ represents the heat that must be communicated, while the volume alters by dv and $d\theta = 0$. In the application to radiation M cannot vanish, and therefore p cannot. In this case clearly

$$M = U + p \tag{30}$$

where U denotes the volume-density of the energy—a function of θ only. Hence

$$\theta \frac{dp}{d\theta} = U + p. \tag{31}$$

If we assume from electromagnetic theory that

$$p = \tfrac{1}{3}U, \tag{32}$$

it follows at once that

$$U \propto \theta^4, \tag{33}$$

the well-known law of Stefan.

In (31) if p be known as a function of θ, U as a function of θ follows immediately. If, on the other hand, U be known, we have

$$d\left(\frac{p}{\theta}\right) = \frac{U}{\theta^2}\,d\theta,$$

and thence

$$\frac{p}{\theta} = \int_0^\theta \frac{U}{\theta^2}\,d\theta + C. \tag{34}$$

* "On the Pressure of Vibrations," *Phil. Mag.* Vol. III, p. 338, 1902. [Art. 276.]

On the Pressure Developed in a Liquid During the Collapse of a Spherical Cavity (1917)

[*Philosophical Magazine* Vol. xxxiv, pp. 94–98, 1917]

Editorial Preface

This is a relatively early paper in the field of cavitation which continues to attract a great deal of attention in modern research in acoustics and hydrodynamics. Here Rayleigh shows how from fairly simple considerations one can calculate theoretically the rather high pressures produced in a liquid through the collapse of a cavitation bubble.

When reading O. Reynold's description of the sounds emitted by water in a kettle as it comes to the boil, and their explanation as due to the partial or complete collapse of bubbles as they rise through cooler water, I proposed to myself a further consideration of the problem thus presented; but I had not gone far when I learned from Sir C. Parsons that he also was interested in the same question in connexion with cavitation behind screw-propellers, and that at his instigation Mr S. Cook, on the basis of an investigation by Besant, had calculated the pressure developed when the collapse is suddenly arrested by impact against a rigid concentric obstacle. During the collapse the fluid is regarded as incompressible.

In the present note I have given a simpler derivation of Besant's results, and have extended the calculation to find the pressure in the interior of the fluid during the collapse. It appears that before the cavity is closed these pressures may rise very high in the fluid near the inner boundary.

As formulated by Besant*, the problem is—

"An infinite mass of homogeneous incompressible fluid acted

* Besant's *Hydrostatics and Hydrodynamics*, 1859, § 158.

H

upon by no forces is at rest, and a spherical portion of the fluid is suddenly annihilated; it is required to find the instantaneous alteration of pressure at any point of the mass, and the time in which the cavity will be filled up, the pressure at an infinite distance being supposed to remain constant."

Since the fluid is incompressible, the whole motion is determined by that of the inner boundary. If U be the velocity and R the radius of the boundary at time t, and u the simultaneous velocity at any distance r (greater than R) from the centre, then

$$u/U = R^2/r^2;\qquad(1)$$

and if ρ be the density, the whole kinetic energy of the motion is

$$\tfrac{1}{2}\rho \int_R^\infty u^2 \,.\, 4\pi r^2 \,dr = 2\pi\rho U^2 R^3.\qquad(2)$$

Again, if P be the pressure at infinity and R_0 the initial value of R, the work done is

$$\frac{4\pi P}{3}(R_0{}^3 - R^3).\qquad(3)$$

When we equate (2) and (3) we get

$$U^2 = \frac{2P}{3\rho}\left(\frac{R_0{}^3}{R^3} - 1\right),\qquad(4)$$

expressing the velocity of the boundary in terms of the radius. Also, since $U = dR/dt$,

$$t = \sqrt{\left(\frac{3\rho}{2P}\right)} \,.\, \int_R^{R_0} \frac{(R^{3/2}dR)}{(R_0{}^3 - R^3)^{\frac{1}{2}}} = R_0 \sqrt{\left(\frac{3\rho}{2P}\right)} \,.\, \int_\beta^1 \frac{\beta^{3/2}d\beta}{(1 - \beta^3)^{\frac{1}{2}}}\qquad(5)$$

if $\beta = R/R_0$. The time of collapse to a given fraction of the original radius is thus proportional to $R_0\rho^{\frac{1}{2}}P^{-\frac{1}{2}}$, a result which might have been anticipated by a consideration of "dimensions". The time τ of *complete* collapse is obtained by making $\beta = 0$ in (5). An equivalent expression is given by Besant, who refers to Cambridge Senate House Problems of 1847.

Writing $\beta^3 = z$, we have

$$\int_0^1 \frac{\beta^{3/2}d\beta}{(1-\beta^3)^{\frac{1}{2}}} = \tfrac{1}{3}\int_0^1 z^{-1/6}(1-z)^{-\frac{1}{2}}\,dz,$$

which may be expressed by means of Γ functions. Thus

$$\tau = R_0\sqrt{\left(\frac{\rho}{6P}\right)}\cdot\frac{\Gamma(\tfrac{5}{6})\cdot\Gamma(\tfrac{1}{2})}{\Gamma(\tfrac{4}{3})} = \cdot 91468R_0\sqrt{(\rho/P)}. \qquad (6)$$

According to (4) U increases without limit as R diminishes. This indefinite increase may be obviated if we introduce, instead of an internal pressure zero or constant, one which increases with sufficient rapidity. We may suppose such a pressure due to a permanent gas obedient to Boyle's law. Then, if the initial pressure be Q, the work of compression is $4\pi QR_0^3\log(R_0/R)$, which is to be subtracted from (3). Hence

$$U^2 = \frac{2P}{3\rho}\left(\frac{R_0^3}{R^3}-1\right) - \frac{2Q}{\rho}\frac{R_0^3}{R^3}\log\frac{R_0}{R}\,; \qquad (7)$$

and $U = 0$ when

$$P(1-z) + Q\log z = 0, \qquad (8)$$

z denoting (as before) the ratio of volumes R^3/R_0^3. Whatever be the (positive) value of Q, U comes again to zero before complete collapse, and if $Q > P$ the first movement of the boundary is outwards. The boundary oscillates between two positions, of which one is the initial.

The following values of P/Q are calculated from (8):

z	P/Q	z	P/Q
$\frac{1}{1000}$	6·9147	1	arbitrary
$\frac{1}{100}$	4·6517	2	0·6931
$\frac{1}{10}$	2·5584	4	0·4621
$\frac{1}{4}$	1·8484	10	0·2558
$\frac{1}{2}$	1·3863	100	0·0465
1	arbitrary	1000	0·0069

Reverting to the case where the pressure inside the cavity is zero, or at any rate constant, we may proceed to calculate the pressure at any internal point. The general equation of pressure is

$$\frac{1}{\rho}\frac{dp}{dr} = -\frac{Du}{Dt} = -\frac{du}{dt} - u\frac{du}{dr}, \tag{9}$$

u being a function of r and t, reckoned positive in the direction of increasing r. As in (1), $u = UR^2/r^2$, and

$$\frac{du}{dt} = \frac{1}{r^2}\frac{d}{dt}(UR^2).$$

Also

$$\frac{d(UR^2)}{dt} = 2R\frac{dR}{dt}U + R^2\frac{dU}{dt} = 2RU^2 + R^2\frac{dU}{dt},$$

and by (4)

$$\frac{dU}{dt} = -\frac{P}{\rho}\frac{R_0^3}{R^4},$$

so that

$$\frac{d(UR^2)}{dt} = 2RU^2 - \frac{P}{\rho}\frac{R_0^3}{R^2}.$$

Thus, suitably determining the constant of integration, we get

$$\frac{p}{P} - 1 = \frac{R}{3r}\left\{\frac{R_0^3}{R^3} - 4\right\} - \frac{R^4}{3r^4}\left\{\frac{R_0^3}{R^3} - 1\right\}. \tag{10}$$

At the first moment after release, when $R = R_0$, we have

$$p = P(1 - R_0/r). \tag{11}$$

When $r = R$, that is on the boundary, $p = 0$, whatever R may be, in accordance with assumptions already made.

Initially the maximum p is at infinity, but as the contraction proceeds, this ceases to be true. If we introduce z to represent R_0^3/R^3, (10) may be written

$$\frac{p}{P} - 1 = \frac{R}{3r}(z - 4) - \frac{R^4}{3r^4}(z - 1), \tag{12}$$

and

$$\frac{dp/P}{dr} = \frac{R}{3r^2}\left\{\frac{(4z-4)R^3}{r^3} - (z-4)\right\}. \tag{13}$$

The maximum value of p occurs when

$$\frac{r^3}{R^3} = \frac{4z-4}{z-4}; \tag{14}$$

and then

$$\frac{p}{P} = 1 + \frac{(z-4)R}{4r} = 1 + \frac{(z-4)^{4/3}}{4^{4/3}(z-1)^{1/3}}. \tag{15}$$

So long as z, which always exceeds 1, is less than 4, the greatest value of p, viz. P, occurs at infinity; but when z exceeds 4, the maximum p occurs at a finite distance given by (14) and is greater than P. As the cavity fills up, z becomes great, and (15) approxi-mates to

$$\frac{p}{P} = \frac{z}{4^{4/3}} = \frac{R_0^3}{4^{4/3}R^3}, \tag{16}$$

corresponding to

$$r = 4^{\frac{1}{3}}R = 1\cdot587R. \tag{17}$$

It appears from (16) that before complete collapse the pressure near the boundary becomes very great. For example, if $R = \frac{1}{20}R_0$, $p = 1260P$.

This pressure occurs at a relatively moderate distance outside the boundary. At the boundary itself the pressure is zero, so long as the motion is free. Mr Cook considers the pressure here developed when the fluid strikes an absolutely rigid sphere of radius R. If the supposition of incompressibility is still main-tained, an infinite pressure momentarily results; but if at this stage we admit compressibility, the instantaneous pressure P' is finite, and is given by the equation

$$\frac{P'^2}{2\beta'} = \tfrac{1}{2}\rho U^2 = \frac{P}{3}\left(\frac{R_0^3}{R^3} - 1\right), \tag{18}$$

β' being the coefficient of compressibility. P, P', β' may all be expressed in atmospheres. Taking (as for water) $\beta' = 20,000$, $= 1$, and $R = \frac{1}{20}R_0$, Cook finds

$$P' = 10,300 \text{ atmospheres} = 68 \text{ tons per sq. inch,}$$

and it would seem that this conclusion is not greatly affected by the neglect of compressibility before impact.

The subsequent course of events might be traced as in *Theory of Sound*, § 279, but it would seem that for a satisfactory theory compressibility would have to be taken into account at an earlier stage.

Presidential Address to
the Society for Psychical Research (1919)

[*Proceedings of the Society for Psychical Research*, Vol. xxx, pp. 275–290, 1919]

Editorial Preface

Rayleigh accepted the Presidency of the Society for Psychical Research and gave the presidential address the year of his death. The address is here reprinted in full with the purpose of emphasizing Rayleigh's open-mindedness with respect to aspects of human experience in which strict scientific investigation is difficult. It is of interest to note his cautious attitude toward psychical phenomena, his reservations with respect to their validity but at the same time his feeling that further research in this field is desirable. His remarks on telepathy are particularly relevant in the light of recent studies of so-called extrasensory perception.

Before entering upon the matters that I had intended to lay before you, it is fitting that I should refer to the loss we have sustained within the last few days in the death of Sir William Crookes, a former President of the Society during several years from 1896–1899, and a man of world-wide scientific reputation. During his long and active life he made many discoveries in Physics and Chemistry of the first importance. In quite early days his attention was attracted by an unknown and brilliant green line in the spectrum, which he succeeded in tracing to a new element named Thallium, after its appearance. Later he was able so to improve vacua as to open up fresh lines of inquiry with remarkable results in more than one direction. The radiometer, a little instrument in which light, even candle-light, or ordinary day-light, causes the rotation of delicately suspended vanes, presents problems even yet only partially solved. And his discoveries relating to electric discharge in high vacua lie near the foundation of the modern theories of electricity as due to minute charged particles called electrons, capable of separation from ordinary chemical atoms, and of moving with speeds of the order of the speed of light. One is struck not only by the technical skill displayed in experiments more difficult at the time they were made than the younger generation of workers can easily understand, but also by the extraordinary instinct which directed Crookes' choice of subjects. In several cases their importance was hardly realized at the time, and only later became apparent.

I shall have occasion presently to notice in some little detail his early "Notes on Phenomena called Spiritual". It was these that attracted my own attention to the subject. In 1889 he published further "Notes of Séances with D. D. Home" in Vol. vi. of our *Proceedings*. I fancy that he was disappointed with the reception that his views met with, having been sanguine enough to expect that he would obtain the same credence when he wrote on psychical matters as when he was dealing with Physics or Chemistry. In later years I understand he did not often introduce the subject, but when questioned was firm that he had nothing to retract. One would give much to know whether this attitude is still maintained.

Any hesitation that I may have felt in undertaking the honourable office to which you have called me was largely due to the fact that I have no definite conclusions to announce, and that such experiences as I have had were long ago, and can hardly now carry weight as evidence to anyone but myself. But I have always taken an interest in questions such as those considered by the Society, and I may perhaps as well give a short account of what I have seen, for it will at any rate help to explain my attitude and serve as a foundation for comment.

I may begin with what is now called hypnotism. This is an old story; but many have forgotten, or never realized, the disbelief which was general in the fifties of the last century both on the part of the public and of medical men. As to the former, reference may be made to *Punch**, and as to the latter I suppose there can be no doubt, although of course there were distinguished exceptions. At the present day orthodox medical opinion has so far shifted its ground as to claim for the profession control of what was formerly dismissed as impossible and absurd—certainly a less unreasonable position.

It was some ten or eleven years from the date of *Punch's* cartoon that I witnessed in a friend's rooms at Cambridge an exhibition of the powers of Madame Card. I think eight or ten of us were tried, including myself. We were made to gaze for a time at a "magnetic" disk; afterwards she made passes over our closed eyes, and finally defied us to open them. I and some others experienced no difficulty; and naturally she discarded us and developed her powers over those—about half the sitters— who failed or found difficulty. Among the latter were personal friends of my own and two well-known University athletes. One was told that he could not give his name, another that he would have to cross the room towards her when she beckoned, and so on. In spite of obvious efforts to resist her influence they had to obey. In conversation afterwards they assured me that they could not help it; and indeed they made such fools of themselves that I had no difficulty in believing them. From that evening I have never felt any doubt as to the possibility of influencing unwilling minds by suggestion; and I have often wished that on other occasions, where dubious phenomena were in question, some of which I shall presently refer to, conviction one way or the other had followed this precedent. I ought to add that, although stories were afloat to that effect, I never saw the influence of Madame Card conveyed otherwise than by word or gesture.

After this experience I was not disinclined to believe that what was, or at any rate had recently been, orthodox opinion might be quite wrong, and accordingly became interested in what I heard

* Vol. xxiv, p. 120 (1853).—*Lecturer on Electro-Biology.* "Now, Sir! You can't jump over that Stick! Ahem!" *Subject.* "Jump? Eh! Ugh! Lor bless me, Jump? No, I know I can't—never could jump—Ugh!"

[*Thunders of Applause from the Gentlemen in the cane-bottom chairs*—(*i.e. believers*)].

from friends of the doings of Home and other so-called mediums. Some of the stories could, as it seemed, be explained away only on the supposition of barefaced lying, or more charitably as the result of hallucination, whether self-induced, or due to the suggestion and influence of others. The possibility of the latter view cannot be left out of account, but I have never seen anything to show that it has the remotest application to my own experience or that of the friends with whom I have co-operated.

The interest that I felt was greatly stimulated by the appearance of Sir W. Crookes' "Notes of an Enquiry into the Phenomena called Spiritual during the years 1870–73*". I was acquainted with some of the author's scientific work, and knew that he was a skilful experimenter and likely to be alive to the precautions required in order to guard against sense illusions. Presumably also he would feel the difficulty of accepting conclusions so much out of harmony with ordinary and laboratory experience. If heavy tables in a dining-room can leave the floor, how is it that in the laboratory our balances can be trusted to deal with a tenth of a milligram?

I have lately read over again Sir W. Crookes' article, and I do not wonder at the impression it produced upon me. I am tempted to quote one or two passages against which I find my old pencil marks. Under the heading—The Appearance of Hands, either Self-luminous or Visible by Ordinary Light, he writes, "I have retained one of these hands in my own, firmly resolved not to let it escape. There was no struggle or effort made to get loose, but it gradually seemed to resolve itself into vapour, and faded in that manner from my grasp." I believe that the rationalistic explanation is that the hand was an inflated glove, like a rubber balloon, from which the air gradually leaked away, but I gave Sir W. Crookes credit for being able to retain the rubber.

Another incident of an entirely different character is thus described. "A lady was writing automatically by means of the planchette. I was trying to devise a means of proving that what she wrote was not due to 'unconscious cerebration'. The planchette,

* *Quarterly Journal of Science*, Jan. 1874.

as it always does, insisted that, although it was moved by the hand and arm of the lady, the *intelligence* was that of an invisible being who was playing on her brain as on a musical instrument, and thus moving her muscles. I therefore said to this intelligence, 'Can you see the contents of this room?' 'Yes,' wrote the planchette. 'Can you see to read this newspaper?' said I, putting my finger on a copy of the *Times*, which was on the table behind me, but without looking at it. 'Yes,' was the reply of the planchette. 'Well,' I said, 'if you can see that, write the word which is now covered by my finger, and I will believe you.' The planchette commenced to move. Slowly and with great difficulty, the word 'however' was written. I turned round, and saw the word 'however' was covered by the tip of my finger."

"I had purposely avoided looking at the newspaper when I tried this experiment, and it was impossible for the lady, had she tried, to have seen any of the printed words, for she was sitting at one table, and the paper was on another table behind, my body intervening."

The two mediums whose names are mentioned in the article, and with whom most of the observations were made, are Home and Miss Fox, afterwards Mrs Jencken. A highly desirable characteristic of Home's mediumship was the unusual opportunity allowed to the sense of sight. Home always objected to darkness at his séances. "Indeed," says Sir William Crookes, "except on two occasions . . . everything that I have witnessed with him has taken place in the light."

I found (and indeed still find) it difficult to accept what one may call the "knave and fool theory" of these occurrences; but failing that, it would seem to follow that one must admit the possibility of much that contrasts strongly with ordinary experience, and I was naturally anxious to obtain first hand information on which I could form an independent judgment. Home was no longer available, but I was able to obtain the co-operation of Mrs Jencken, who stayed in my country house as guest during two or three visits extending altogether, I suppose, over fourteen days or so. She was accompanied by a nurse and baby, and for a small part of the time by Mr Jencken, who seemed curiously slow to understand that we had to regard him as well as his wife with suspicion, when I explained that we could not attach importance to séances when both were present. It may be well to add that they received nothing beyond the usual courtesy and entertainment due to guests.

The results were upon the whole disappointing, and certainly far short of those described by Sir W. Crookes. Nevertheless, there was a good deal not easy to explain away. Very little of importance occurred in a good light. It is true that at any hour of the day Mrs Jencken was able to get raps upon a door by merely placing her fingers upon it. The listener, hearing them for the first time, felt sure there was someone on the other side, but it was not so. The closest scrutiny revealed no movement of her fingers, but there seemed nothing to exclude the possibility of bone-cracking with the door acting as sounding-board. However, on one or two occasions loud thumps were heard, such as one would hardly like to make with one's knee. With the exception of her fingers Mrs Jencken seemed always to stand quite clear, and the light was good.

On the other hand, during séances the light was usually bad—gas turned very low. But in some other respects the conditions may be considered good. Before commencing, the room was searched and the doors locked. Besides Mrs Jencken, the sitters were usually Lady Rayleigh and myself. Sometimes a brother or a friend came. We sat close together at a small, but rather heavy, pedestal table; and when anything appeared to be doing we held Mrs Jencken's hands, with a good attempt to control her feet also with ours; but it was impracticable to maintain this full control during all the long time occupied by the séances. In contrast to some other mediums, Mrs Jencken was not observed to fidget or to try to release her limbs.

As I have said, the results were disappointing; but I do not mean that very little happened or that what did happen was always easy to explain. But most of the happenings were trifling, and not such as to preclude the idea of trickery. One's coat-tails would be pulled, paper cutters, etc., would fly about, knocks would shake our chairs, and so on. I do not count messages, usually of no interest, which were spelt out alphabetically by raps that seemed to come from the neighbourhood of the medium's feet. Perhaps what struck us most were lights which on one or two occasions floated about. They were real enough, but rather difficult to locate, though I do not think they were ever more than six or eight feet away from us. Like some of those described by Sir W. Crookes, they might be imitated by phosphorus enclosed in cotton wool; but how Mrs Jencken could manipulate them with her hands and feet held, and it would seem with only her mouth at liberty, is a difficulty.

Another incident hard to explain occurred at the close of a séance after we had all stood up. The table at which we had been sitting gradually tipped over until the circular top nearly touched the floor, and then slowly rose again into the normal position. Mrs Jencken, as well as outselves, was apparently standing quite clear of it. I have often tried since to make the table perform a similar evolution. Holding the top with both hands, I can make some, though a bad, approximation; but it was impossible that Mrs Jencken could have worked it thus. Possibly something better could be done with the aid of an apparatus of hooks and wires; but Mrs Jencken was a small woman, without much apparent muscular development, and the table for its size is heavy. It must be admitted that the light was poor, but our eyes were then young, and we had been for a long time in the semi-darkness.

In common, I suppose, with most witnesses of such things, I repudiate altogether the idea of hallucination as an explanation. The incidents were almost always unexpected, and our impressions of them agreed. They were either tricks of the nature of conjuring tricks, or else happenings of a kind very remote from ordinary experience.

A discouraging feature was that attempts to improve the conditions usually led to nothing. As an example, I may mention that after writing, supposed to be spirit writing, had appeared, I arranged pencils and paper inside a large glass retort, of which the neck was then hermetically sealed. For safety this was placed in a wooden box, and stood under the table during several séances. The intention was to give opportunity for evidence that would be independent of close watching during the semi-darkness. It is perhaps unnecessary to say that though scribbling appeared on the box, there was nothing inside the retort. Possibly this was too much to expect. I may add that on recently inspecting the retort I find that the opportunity has remained neglected for forty-five years.

During all this time I have been in doubt what interpretation to put upon these experiences. In my judgment the incidents were not good enough, or under good enough conditions, to establish occult influences; but yet I have always felt difficulty in accepting the only alternative explanation. Some circumstances, if of secondary importance, are also worthy of mention. Unlike some other mediums that I have known, Mrs Jencken never tried to divert one's attention, nor did she herself seem to be observant or watching for opportunities. I have often said that on the unfavourable hypothesis her acting was as wonderful as her conjuring. Seldom, or never, during the long hours we were together at meals or séances did she make an intelligent remark. Her interests seemed to be limited to the spirits and her baby.

Mr Jencken is another difficulty. He, an intelligent man, was a spiritualist, and, I have no reason to doubt, an honest one, before he married his wife. Could she have continued to deceive him? It seems almost impossible. He bore eye-witness to the baby—at the age of three months I think it was—taking a pencil and writing a spirit message, of which we saw what purported to be a photograph. If, on the other hand, he had found her out, would he have permitted her to continue her deceptions?

After the death of Home and Mrs Jencken, so-called physical manifestations of a well attested kind seem rather to have fallen into abeyance, except in the case of Eusapia Palladino. Although I attended one or two of her séances at Cambridge and saw a few curious things, other members of the Society have had so much better opportunities that I pass them by. There is no doubt that she practised deception, but that is not the last word.

One of the difficulties which beset our inquiry is the provoking attitude of many people who might render assistance. Some see nothing out of the way in the most marvellous occurrences, and accordingly take no pains over the details of evidence on which everything depends. Others attribute all these things to the devil, and refuse to have anything to say to them. I have sometimes pointed out that if during the long hours of séances we could keep the devil occupied in so comparatively harmless a manner we deserved well of our neighbours.

A real obstacle to a decision arises from the sporadic character of the phenomena, which cannot be reproduced at pleasure and submitted to systematic experimental control. The difficulty is not limited to questions where occult influences may be involved. This is a point which is often misunderstood, and it may be worth while to illustrate it by examples taken from the history of science.

An interesting case is that of meteorites, discussed by Sir L. Fletcher, formerly Keeper of Minerals in the British Museum, from whose official pamphlet (published in 1896) some extracts may be quoted:—"1. Till the beginning of the present [*i.e.* 19th] century, the fall of stones from the sky was an event, the actuality of which neither men of science nor the mass of the people could be brought to believe in. Yet such falls have been recorded from the earliest times, and the records have occasionally been received as authentic by a whole nation. In general, however, the witnesses of such an event have been treated with the disrespect usually shown to reporters of the extraordinary, and have been laughed at for their supposed delusions: this is less to be wondered at when we remember that the witnesses of a fall have usually been few in number, unaccustomed to exact observation, frightened by what they both saw and heard, and have had a common tendency towards exaggeration and superstition."

After mention of some early stones, he continues:

"3. These falls from the sky, when credited at all, have been deemed prodigies or miracles, and the stones have been regarded as objects for reverence and worship. It has even been conjectured that the worship of such stones was the earliest form of idolatry... The Diana of the Ephesians, 'which fell down from Jupiter,' and the image of Venus at Cyprus appear to have been, not statues, but conical or pyramidal stones."

"5. Three French Academicians, one of whom was the afterwards renowned chemist Lavoisier, presented to the Academy in 1772 a report on the analysis of a stone said to have been seen to fall at Lucé on September 13, 1768. As the identity of lightning with the electric spark had been recently established by Franklin, they were in advance convinced that 'thunder-stones' existed only in the imagination; and never dreaming of the existence of a 'sky-stone' which had no relation to a 'thunder-stone', they somewhat easily assured both themselves and the Academy that there was nothing unusual in the mineralogical characters of the Lucé specimen, their verdict being that the stone was an ordinary one which had been struck by lightning."

"6. In 1794 the German philosopher Chladni, famed for his researches into the laws of sound, brought together numerous accounts of the fall of bodies from the sky, and called the attention of the scientific world to the fact that several masses of iron, of which he specially considers two, had in all probability come from outer space to this planet."

In 1802 Edward Howard read a paper before the Royal Society of London giving an account of the comparative results of a chemical and mineralogical investigation of four stones which had fallen in different places. He found from the similarity of their component parts "very strong evidence in favour of the assertion that they had fallen on our globe. They have been found at places very remote from each other, and at periods also sufficiently distant. The mineralogists who have examined them agree that they have no resemblance to mineral substances properly so called, nor have they been described by mineralogical authors." After this quotation from Howard, Fletcher continues:

"13. This paper aroused much interest in the scientific world, and, though Chladni's theory that such stones come from outer space was still not accepted in France, it was there deemed more of worthy consideration after Poisson (following Laplace) had shown that a body shot from the moon in the direction of the earth, with an initial velocity of 7592 feet a second, would not fall back upon the moon, but would actually, after a journey of sixty-four hours, reach the earth, upon which, neglecting the resistance of the air, it would fall with a velocity of about 31,508 feet a second."

"14. Whilst the minds of the scientific men of France were in this unsettled condition, there came a report that another shower of stones had fallen, this time . . . within easy reach of Paris. To settle the matter finally, if possible, the physicist Biot was directed by the Minister of the Interior to inquire into the event on the spot. After a careful examination . . . Biot was convinced that on Tuesday, April 26, 1803, about 1 p.m., there was a violent *explosion* in the neighbourhood of l'Aigle . . . that some moments before . . . a *fire ball* in quick motion was seen . . . that on the same day many stones fell in the neighbourhood of l'Aigle. Biot estimated the number of the stones at two or three thousand. . . . With the exception of a few little clouds of ordinary character, the sky was quite clear. The exhaustive report of Biot, and the conclusive nature of his proofs, compelled the whole of the scientific world to recognise the fall of stones on the earth from outer space as an undoubted fact."

I commend this history to the notice of those scientific men who are so sure that they understand the character of Nature's operations as to feel justified in rejecting without examination reports of occurrences which seem to conflict with ordinary experience. Every tiro now knows that the stones to be seen in most museums had an origin thought impossible by some of the leading and most instructed men of about a century ago.

Other cases of strange occurrences, the nature or reality of which is, I suppose, still in doubt, are "Globe lightning" and "Will of the wisp". The evidence for globe lightning is fairly substantial, but in the judgment of many scientific men is outweighed by the absence of support in laboratory experience. At one time I was more disposed to believe in it than I am now, in view of the great extension of electrical experimenting during the last thirty years. Kelvin thought it might be explained as an ocular illusion. By a lightning flash the retina is powerfully impressed, it may be excentrically, with the formation of a prolonged positive "spectrum" or image which, as the eye tries to follow it, appears to sail slowly along. Some seconds later, the arrival of the sound of thunder causes a shock, under which the luminous globe disappears and is thought to have burst explosively. I think this explanation, which would save the good faith and to some extent the good sense of the observers, deserves attention.

Then again the Will of the wisp, for which I take it there used to be plenty of evidence. I have been told by the Duke of Argyll—the friend and colleague of Gladstone—that in his youth it was common at Inveraray, but had been less seen latterly, owing, he thought, to drainage operations. Chemists will not readily believe in the spontaneous inflammation of "marsh gas", but I have heard the suggestion made of phosphoric gases arising from the remains of a dead sheep that had got entangled.

The truth is that we are ill equipped for the investigation of phenomena which cannot be reproduced at pleasure under good conditions. And a clue is often necessary before much progress can be made. Men had every motive for trying to understand malaria. Exposure at night on low ground was known to be bad; and it had even been suggested that mosquito nets served as a protection; but before Pasteur, and indeed for some years after, it seems never to have occurred to any one that the mosquito itself was the vehicle. Sir A. Geikie has remarked that until recent times the study of the lower forms of life was regarded with something like contempt. Verily, the microbes have had their revenge.

But when all this has been said we must not forget that the situation is much worse when it is complicated by the attempts of our neighbours to mislead us, as indeed occasionally happens in other matters of scientific interest where money is involved. Here also the questions before this Society differ from most of those dealt with by scientific men, and may often need a different kind of criticism.

Such criticism it has been the constant aim of the Society to exercise, as must be admitted by all who have studied carefully our published matter. If my words could reach them, I would appeal to serious inquirers to give more attention to the work of this Society, conducted by experienced men and women, including several of a sceptical turn of mind, and not to indulge in hasty conclusions on the basis of reports in the less responsible newspaper press or on the careless gossip of ill-informed acquaintances. Many of our members are quite as much alive to *a priori* difficulties as any outsider can be.

Of late years the published work of the Society has dealt rather with questions of another sort, involving telepathy, whether from living or other intelligences, and some of the most experienced and cautious investigators are of opinion that a case has been made out. Certainly some of the cross-correspondences established are very remarkable. Their evaluation, however, requires close attention and sometimes a background of information, classical and other, not at the disposal of all of us. In this department I often find my estimate of probabilities differing from that of my friends. I have more difficulty than they feel over telepathy between the living, but if I had no doubts there I should feel less difficulty than many do in going further. I think emphasis should be laid upon the fact that the majority of scientific men do not believe in telepathy, or even that it is possible. We are very largely the creatures of our sense-organs. Only those physicists and physiologists who have studied the subject realize what wonderful instruments these are. The eye, the ear, and the nose—even the human nose—are hard to beat, and within their proper range are more sensitive than anything we can make in the laboratory. It is true that with long exposures we can photograph objects in the heavens that the eye cannot detect; but the fairer comparison is between what we can see and what can be photographed in say $\frac{1}{10}$th second—all that the eye requires. These sense-organs, shared with the higher animals, must have taken a long time to build up, and one would suppose that much development in other directions must have been sacrificed or postponed in that interest. Why was not telepathy developed until there could be no question about it? Think of an antelope in danger from a lion about to spring upon him, and gloating over the anticipation of his dinner. The antelope is largely protected by the acuteness of his senses and his high speed when alarmed. But would it not have been simpler if he could know something telepathically of the lion's intention, even if it were no more than vague apprehension warning him to be on the move?

By telepathy is to be understood something more than is implied in the derivation of the word, the conveying of feeling or information otherwise than by use of the senses, or at any rate the known senses. Distance comes into the question mainly because it may exclude their ordinary operation. Some appear to think that all difficulty is obviated by the supposition of an unknown physical agency capable of propagating effects from one brain to another, acting like the transmitter and receiver in wireless telegraphy or telephony. On a physical theory of this kind one must expect a rapid attenuation with distance, not suggested by the records. If distance is an important consideration, one might expect husbands and wives with their heads within two or three feet of one another to share their dreams habitually. But there is a more fundamental objection. Specific information is, and can only be, conveyed in this manner by means of a *code*. People seem to forget that all speaking and writing depend upon a code, and that even the voluntary or involuntary indications of feeling by facial expression or gestures involve something of the same nature. It will hardly be argued that telepathy acts by means of the usual code of common language, as written or spoken.

The conclusion that I draw is that no pains should be spared to establish the reality of telepathy on such sure ground that it must be generally admitted by all serious inquirers. It is quite natural that those who have already reached this position should be more interested in the question of communications from the dead. To my mind telepathy with the dead would present comparatively little difficulty when it is admitted as regards the living. If the apparatus of the senses is not used in one case, why should it be needed in the other?

I do not underrate the difficulties of the investigation. Very special conditions must be satisfied if we are to be independent of the good faith of the persons primarily concerned. The performance of the Zanzigs may be recalled. When there could be no question of confederates, answers respecting objects suddenly exhibited were given with such amazing rapidity that secret codes seemed almost excluded. But when a party, in which I was included, attempted to get a repetition under stricter conditions, there was an almost entire failure. Our requirement was simply that the husband should not speak *after* he had seen the object that was to be described by the wife. But I must add the inevitable qualification. Towards the end of the evening cards were correctly told several times, when we were unable to detect anything that could serve as audible signals.

I have dwelt upon the difficulties besetting the acceptance of telepathy, but I fully recognize that a strong case has been made out for it. I hope that more members of the Society will experiment in this direction. It is work that can be done at home, at odd times, and without the help of mediums, professional or other. Some very interesting experiences of this kind have been recorded by a former President, Prof. Gilbert Murray. With perhaps an excess of caution, he abstained from formulating conclusions that must have seemed to most readers to follow from the facts detailed. I trust we may hear still more from him.

It is hardly necessary to emphasize that in evaluating evidence it is quality rather than quantity with which we are concerned. No one can doubt the existence of apparently trustworthy reports of many occult phenomena. For this there must be a reason, and our object is to find it. But whatever it may be, whether reality of the phenomena, or the stupidity or carelessness or worse of the narrators, a larger sweep is sure to add to the material. However, we may hope that such additions will occasionally afford clues, or at least suggestions for further inquiry. And if the phenomena, or any of them, are really due to supernormal causes, further solid evidence of this will emerge. I feel that I ought to apologize for giving utterance to what must seem platitudes to the more experienced working members of the Society.

Some of the narratives that I have read suggest the possibility of prophecy. This is very difficult ground. But we live in times which are revoluntionary in science as well as in politics. Perhaps some of those who accept extreme "relativity" views reducing time to merely one of the dimensions of a four-dimensional manifold, may regard the future as differing from the past no more than north differs from south. But here I am nearly out of my depth, and had better stop.

I fear that my attitude, or want of attitude, will be disappointing to some members of the Society who have out-stripped me on the road to conviction, but this I cannot help. Scientific men should not rush to conclusions, but keep their minds open for such time as may be necessary. And what was at first a policy may become a habit. After forty-five years of hesitation it may require some personal experience of a compelling kind to break the crust. Some of those who know me best think that I ought to be more convinced than I am. Perhaps they are right.

However this may be, I have never felt any doubt as to the importance of the work carried on by the Society over many years, and I speak as one who has examined not a few of the interesting and careful papers that have been published in the *Proceedings*. Several of the founders of the Society were personal friends, and since they have gone the same spirit has guided us. Our goal is the truth, whatever it may turn out to be, and our efforts to attain it should have the sympathy of all, and I would add especially of scientific men.

Index

243